And Life Goes On

Francisco Candido Xavier

And Life Goes On

By the Spirit
Andre Luiz

ISBN: 978-85-7945-004-4

Original title in Portuguese:
E A VIDA CONTINUA...
Brazil, 1968

Translated by: Darrel W. Kimble and Ily Reis

Cover design by: Luciano Carneiro Holanda
Layout: Ingrid Saori Furuta
Photo: www.sxc.hu/claudmey

Edition of
INTERNATIONAL SPIRITIST COUNCIL
SGAN Q. 909 – Conjunto F
70790-090 – Brasilia (DF) – Brazil
www.edicei.com
edicei@edicei.com
+55 61 3038-8400

Sales: + 55 61 3038 8425

Second Edition 8/2011

Authorized edition by Brazilian Spiritist Federation

INTERNATIONAL DATA FOR CATALOGING IN PUBLICATION (ICP)

L979a	Luiz, André (Spirit)
	And Life Goes On / by the Spirit Andre Luiz ; [received by] Francisco Cândido Xavier ; [translated by Darrel W. Kimble and Ily Reis]. - Brasilia, DF (Brazil) : International Spiritist Council, 2011.
	240 p. ; 21 cm
	Translated from: E a Vida Continua...
	ISBN 978-85-7945-004-4
	1. Spiritist Novel. 2. Spiritism. 3. Psychographic Works. I. Xavier, Francisco Cândido, 1910-2002. II. International Spiritist Council. III. Title. IV. Series.

CDD: 133.93
CDU: 133.7

Contents

And life goes on... 7

In Homage 9

1. An Unexpected Meeting 11

2. At the Door to a Close Friendship 17

3. A Friendly Adjustment 23

4. Renewal 29

5. Reunion 37

6. Fraternal Understanding 45

7. Alzira Provides Information 53

8. An Instructive Meeting 59

9. Brother Claudio 67

10. Evelina Serpa 75

11. Ernesto Fantini 83

12. Judgment and Love 91

13. New Tasks 99

14. New Directions 109

15. Time for Analysis 119

16. Renewal Efforts 127

17. Matters of the Heart 135

18. The Return 143

19. Revisions of Life 153

20. The Plot Revealed 163

21. Return to the Past.. 173

22. Bases for a New Future... 183

23. Ernesto at Work 193

24. Evelina at Work.. 205

25. A New Direction.. 217

26. And Life Goes On 225

And life goes on...

Dear reader,

   We are not writing this either to introduce or heap praise on Andre Luiz, the friend who has made himself worthy of our sympathy and gratitude for the consoling and constructive pages he has been sending from the spirit world to the physical.

   However, regarding matters of life "post mortem", it would be fair to say that, in this volume, he brings information that is different from what he garnered in "Nosso Lar," the spirit colony to which he arrived in due course after his discarnation.

   All characters in this account are real personages whose names, of course, have been changed so as not to upset loved ones still on the earth. These characters' experiences are much different than those that describe Andre Luiz's own pathway during his first experiences in the spirit world, and this would lead us to consider that levels of knowledge and responsibility vary infinitely.

   In fact, the planes of existence for the inhabitants of the Beyond are personalized in many different ways, and life for each one is invariably individualized according to their mental condition.

This is understandable.

The greater the learning of an incarnate spirit, the more dolorous the results of time wasted; the more rebellious an individual is before the Truth, the more grievous the consequences of his or her own stubbornness.

Furthermore, we observe that society after death reflects the customs it cultivated while on the earth.

Spirits discarnating from an Asian city do not immediately encounter the customs and buildings of a western city, and vice versa.

A worthy construction does not occur without the cooperation of work and time, just as rashness or violence are not part of the Divine Plans that oversee the universe.

So as not to dwell too long on dispensable remarks, we will only reaffirm the fact that, after our passage into the spirit world, we will find our own spiritual portrait in the situations we forged, either rewarding us for the good they produce or the evil they establish.

Thus, let us read Andre Luiz's new book with the certainty that in its pages we will be startled to find many pieces of our own story in space and time, urging us to meditate and to examine ourselves, realizing that life goes on, filled with hope and work, progress and achievement in every sector of cosmic life in keeping with God's laws.

EMMANUEL
Uberaba, April 18, 1968

In Homage

We honor the First Centennial of Genesis by Allan Kardec.

Andre Luiz
Uberaba, April 18, 1968.

Andre Luiz

1
An Unexpected Meeting

The wind was playing with the dry leaves when Evelina Serpa – Mrs. Serpa – decided to sit on a bench that seemed to be inviting her to rest.

The garden-decorated square was quiet in the silence of the warm afternoon.

There were only a few tourists at the Minas Gerais resort[1] during that second week of October, and among them was Mrs. Serpa, accompanied by an assistant who had remained behind in the hotel room.

Feeling a craving to be alone, Mrs. Serpa had escaped the bustle of domestic life.

She had wanted to think things over. And that is why she was now hiding beneath the green canopy, gazing at the rows of blooming azaleas that took pride in announcing that spring had come.

---

[1] Poços de Caldas, as recalled by characters in chapter 6. It is a resort city located in the Brazilian state of Minas Gerais in southeastern Brazil. Known principally for its thermal baths, it is situated on a stream called Poços de Caldas, near the Pardo River. From http://www.britannica.com/EBchecked/topic/465714/Pocos-de-Caldas – Tr.

Nestled amid the dense foliage, she gave wing to her thoughts...

The family doctor had recommended that she rest to build up her strength before surgery. As she weighed the advantages and risks of the operation, she allowed the memories of her short life to pass through her mind.

She had gotten married six years ago.

At first, everything had been a golden boat ride on waves of blue. A husband and happiness. In their second year of marriage came the pregnancy they had lovingly hoped for; however, along with the pregnancy the disease had appeared. Her body was found to be failing. Her kidneys were incapable of handling any overload and her heart was like an engine about to sputter and quit. Her gynecologist had suggested a therapeutic abortion, and despite the couple's enormous sorrow, the fetus was plucked from the maternal cloister like a baby bird kicked from the nest.

Since then, the journey of her life had become a pathway of tears. Caio, her husband, had metamorphosed into a courteous friend who no longer had any romantic interest in her. He had easily fallen under the spell of another: a young, single woman, whose intelligence and vivaciousness Evelina could deduce from the notes he forgot about in his pockets, and which were filled with passionate words and kisses imprinted on the paper by her red lipstick.

The loneliness and disenchantment she endured at home were perhaps the factors that unleashed the dreadful bouts of overwhelming heaviness she periodically felt in her chest. On such occasions she experienced nausea, excruciating headaches, an overall cold feeling, a burning sensation in her hands and feet, and a noticeable rise in blood pressure. At the height of her agony, she thought she was about to die. Soon thereafter, however, she would recover, only to fall into the same critical condition a few days later when the setbacks with her husband were repeated.

Her energy had deteriorated, her strength was waning...

For more than two years she had gone from doctor to doctor, from specialist to specialist.

The unanimous diagnosis had finally arrived. Only a risky surgical procedure might possibly restore her health.

Deep down, something was telling her intuitively that this physical problem was very serious indeed and could perhaps lead to her death.

Who really knew for sure? she asked herself.

She could hear the chirping sparrows, whose voices provided background music for her thoughts, and she began evaluating her life in terms of aspirations and failures.

Was it really worth it to avoid the dangerous surgery only to continue as a sick woman living with a man who had disregarded his marital vows? And wasn't it reasonable to accept the aid that medical science might offer her so that she could recover her health and fight for a new life in case her husband deserted her completely? She was only twenty-six years old. Wasn't it right for her to wait for new routes to happiness in the fields of time? Although she missed her father tremendously – he had discarnated when she was still a very small child – she had been brought up as an only child by her loving, devoted mother, who in turn had provided her with a kind and caring stepfather. These two, along with her husband, were her entire family back home.

Immersed in the soft breezes of the sunset, she thought of her loved ones: her husband, her dear mother and her stepfather far away.

Suddenly, she remembered her deceased father and her baby that had been taken before being born. She was religious, a practicing Roman Catholic, and as for life after death, she held to the ideas that were fundamental to her faith.

Where might her father and child be right now? she wondered. If she were to die because of her disease, would she see them again? If so, where? Wasn't it reasonable to think about this since the idea of death was constantly on her mind?

She was deeply immersed in this inner monologue when somebody appeared in front of her. It was an older gentleman, whose friendly smile immediately piqued her interest and curiosity.

"Mrs. Serpa?" he asked respectfully.

As she nodded in startled confirmation, he added:

"Please forgive me for being so bold, but I heard that you live in Sao Paulo. So do I. Through highly unexpected circumstances, a friend told me that you and I both have the same health problem."

"I would love to hear about it," said the young woman, noticing his embarrassment.

In response to the kindness in her voice, he introduced himself:

"Nothing to be alarmed about, Mrs. Serpa; Ernesto Fantini, at your service."

"Pleased to meet you," said Evelina, and gazing at that wrinkled, disease-stricken face, she added: "Sit down and rest. Here we are in this huge square, and apparently we're the only ones presently interested in the refreshing atmosphere it has to offer."

Encouraged by her friendliness, Fantini sat down next to her and continued to speak, engaging in a dialog guided by mutual attraction.

"The owner of the hotel where we're staying made friends with your assistant. I found out through her that you too are facing a difficult surgery."

"Too?"

"Yes, because I myself am in the same situation."

"Oh?"

"My blood pressure is out of sync and my whole body is out of whack. I have been seeing specialists for over three years now. Finally, the X-Rays' verdict: I have an adrenal gland tumor. I suspect it's quite serious."

"I see," replied Evelina hesitatingly, looking very pale; "I know just what you mean ... You don't have to tell me. Every so often you must experience the same symptoms: your chest tightens; your heartbeat goes crazy; your head and stomach hurt; the veins in your neck pop out; you feel cold and hot at the same time, and death seems to be at the door."

"Exactly."

"Then, you feel better for a while, only to have it start all over again the next time you get upset."

"You know what it's like."

"Unfortunately."

"The doctor told me the name of my disease a number of times. What about yours?"

Fantini took a tiny notebook from his pocket and read aloud the exact word that defined his health problem.

Mrs. Serpa could barely disguise her discomfort on hearing that scientific term, but getting a hold of herself, she confirmed:

"Yes, speaking for my doctor, my husband told me that's what I have."

The newcomer realized how troubled Evelina was and tried to be humorous:

"Well, at least we have a disease with a rare and pretty name."

"Which doesn't mean we don't suffer frequent and ugly symptoms," she replied charmingly.

Fantini looked up at the blue afternoon sky as if he wanted to take the conversation to the next level. Evelina followed his pause in emotion-filled silence, showing that she too felt like lifting the conversation above the suffering and that she was eager to reflect and philosophize.

2
At the Door to a
Close Friendship

Soon thereafter, a small carriage came into sight, moving very, very slowly.

As he watched the horse gradually drawing nearer, the gentleman asked Evelina:

"I know you need to rest, but if you would accept my invitation for a trip around the thermal springs…"

"Thank you," she responded, "but I can't; for now, rest is the best medicine."

"True. Our case doesn't allow for any bumps on the road."

The small carriage passed by very close to the quiet nook.

Both of them saw why it was moving so slowly. It had evidently been in an accident and displayed a broken wheel as it moved along with difficulty. Meanwhile, the young coachman was on foot guiding the animal with great care, leaving it almost rein-free.

Mrs. Serpa and her new friend followed them with their gaze until they disappeared around the next corner.

Fantini smiled broadly and said calmly:

"Mrs. Serpa…"

She cut him short with another open smile and corrected him in a friendly tone:

"Call me Evelina. I believe that since we both share a rare disease, we have the right to a casual friendship."

"Fine with me!" said Fantini and he added, "And from now on, I shall be just Ernesto to you."

He rested his pale hand on the back of the large bench and continued:

"Dona[2] Evelina, have you ever read anything about spiritualism?"

"No."

"Well, I would like to tell you that that carriage reminded me of some notes I took yesterday while I was studying. The interesting writer I've been reading, though using a definition that he himself considers superficial, understands the human being to be three-fold, much like the carriage, the horse and the coachman, the three of them working together."

"How could that be?" asked Evelina accentuating her surprise and looking at him jokingly.

"The carriage would correspond to the physical body; the animal may be compared to the spiritual body, that is, the molder and sustainer of the phenomena that ensure our physical life; and the coachman symbolizes our spirit, that is, our true self in the mental governance of our life. A damaged 'carriage', like the one we just saw, would represent a sick body, and when the vehicle becomes completely useless, the driver abandons it to the scrap

---

[2] In Brazilian society, *Dona* is a term of respect that is used with the woman's first name. – Tr.

heap of nature and climbs back up on the horse so that both of them may continue the journey ... This, of course, happens at death or discarnation. Now useless, the physical body is returned to the ground, whereas our spirit, clothed in the envelope of subtle matter that conditions its earthly existence, then begins to live on another plane, where the garment of denser matter is no longer useful."

Evelina laughed, though with all due respect for the speaker, and argued:

"A clever theory! You talk about death, but what happens to this trio while we are asleep?"

"For good reasons, during physical sleep the three elements take a rest that varies from driver to driver, or rather, from spirit to spirit. When we sleep, the heavy vehicle or physical body always rests, but the spirit behaves much, much differently. For instance, after the driver and the horse have had a heavy meal, both of them will rest, and consequently, so will the carriage. On the other hand, if the coachman is in the habit of studying and serving, then while the carriage is in the shop for repairs or an overhaul, he uses the horse for instructive trips or worthwhile tasks. At other times, if the driver is still quite unskilled, inexperienced or fearful of the trip, then whenever the carriage needs repairs, he will probably hang around somewhere near the repair shop, waiting for the carriage to be fixed in order to take it up again, much like armor for self-defense."

Evelina showed disbelief and objected:

"I don't know a thing about spiritualism."

"Do you profess any religion in particular?"

"Yes, I'm Catholic. I'm not a fanatic, but I try very hard to live according to the principles of my faith. I believe in our priests' teachings and practice them."

"Good for you. All sincere beliefs are to be respected. I envy your absolute trust."

"You're not religious?"

"I wish I was. I'm just a searcher for the truth, a free shooter in the field of ideas."

"And you've been reading about spiritualism just to entertain yourself?"

"To entertain myself? Oh, no! I read about it because I have to. Have you forgotten, Dona Evelina? We're about to undergo a surgery that could be fatal ... We might be packing our bags for *a very long trip*!

"From which nobody returns."

"Who knows?"

"I get it," smiled the young woman. "You study spiritualism like a traveler who wants to learn about the currency, language, customs and fashion of the foreign country he intends to visit. Concise information, a quick course."

"I admit it. I've had a lot of time on my hands lately, and I'm using it as best I can in everything that relates to the knowledge of the soul, especially life after death and communication with spirits, the supposed inhabitants of other spheres."

"And have you found any proof of such communication? Have you had any direct messages from any of your dead loved ones?"

"Not yet."

"Isn't that discouraging?"

"Not at all!"

"Well, I prefer my serene beliefs. Trust without doubt, prayer without mental torment."

"Your inner faith is a blessing and I sincerely respect your religious contentment; but what if there is another life waiting for us and what if questions do arise in your soul?"

"How can you say that if you haven't yet gotten the confirmation that we do go on living?"

"I cannot doubt the testimonies of the scholars and people of irreproachable character who have confirmed it."

"Well," said Evelina good-naturedly, "you shall be with your researchers and I with my saints."

"I have no objections about the excellence of your advocates," replied Fantini in the same tone, "but I cannot stop my thirst for knowledge. Before I got this disease, I was extremely confident about life. I was in charge and didn't have the faintest idea about the existence of this or that organ in my body. However, a tumor in the adrenal glands is nothing to sneeze at. It is a sort of ghost announcing difficulties and forcing me to think, reason, discover."

"Are you afraid of dying?" joked the young woman.

"Not really; are you?"

"Well, I don't want to die. I have parents, a husband and friends. I love life but..."

"But...?"

"If God has determined that my time is up, I'll resign myself to it."

"Don't you have any other problems?" Haven't you ever suffered the influence of the ills that torment us day after day?"

"Don't tell me you're going to examine my conscience now; I already have to account for myself to my confessors."

And laughing easily, she added:

"I accept the evil others do to us as part of the redemption of our sins before God; however, the bad things we do are stripes that we inflict upon ourselves. As such, I try to watch myself; that is, I realize that I mustn't hurt others. And because of this, I seek in confession an antidote that from time to time inoculates me, preventing my bad inclinations from surfacing."

"It's remarkable that a person of your intelligence would resign herself to confession so willingly and sincerely."

"Of course, I have to choose a priest I can trust. I don't want to buy heaven through calculating means; instead, I want to struggle against my imperfections. That's why it wouldn't be right for me to open up my heart to someone who couldn't understand or help me."

"I see."

Continuing the conversation based on respectful trust, Mrs. Serpa considered:

"Believe me; I too have lived more carefully in light of my disease, so much so, that on the day before coming here, I aligned myself with my religious obligations by going to confession. Of all the matters I entrusted to my old confessor, I can tell you the most important one..."

"No! No! Too much information!" stammered Ernesto, surprised at the caring willingness with which Evelina was expressing herself.

"Why not? We've been talking as if we were old friends. You can tell me how you're preparing for the possibility of death, but I can't talk about mine?"

They both burst out laughing, and during a longer pause in their dialog they looked at each other meaningfully. Both of them looked a bit frightened.

That mutual look told them they had taken a big step toward a close friendship.

"Where had he seen this young woman before, so favored by beauty and intelligence?" wondered Ernesto, puzzled.

"Where could she have met this mature, intelligent gentleman before, who radiated so much sympathy and understanding?" wondered Mrs. Serpa, unable to hide the pleasant surprise that had come over her.

The interlude continued for a few disconcerting seconds while the sunset combined colors and shadows around them, announcing that nightfall was near.

3
A Friendly Adjustment

Fantini realized that Evelina was troubled by the look he had given her and hasted to put her at ease:

"Let's continue, Dona Evelina. I mean you no harm at all. Just look at me; I'm a sick old man, old enough to be your father, and believe me, I see you only as a daughter..."

His voice faded somewhat, but then he recovered and finished:

"The daughter I wish I'd had, instead of the one I do."

Evelina guessed the hidden pain expressed in his words and tried to put him at ease:

"You wouldn't be happy with a sick daughter like me. But ... let's go back to my case, I mean my confession."

"No sad tales..."

"Right. We don't have a lot of time."

And she continued with a playful smile:

"Since we're speaking with such openness in a place that may be death's doorway for either one of us, I can tell you that there's only one thing that troubles me. I've had the same disappointments as anyone else. My father died when I was barely two years old; my widowed mother gave me a stepfather some time later. While still a child, I was sent to a boarding school run by goodly nuns. After that, I married a husband who was much different than what I had dreamed of ... In the middle of our courtship, tragedy struck. Six months before my wedding, a fine young man killed himself because of me. He had attempted suicide once before when he thought I was rejecting him. I felt very sorry for him. I tried to approach him to console him at least, but while my feelings were wavering between him and the man I finally married, he shot himself in the heart. Ever since then, any happiness for me has been like light mixed with darkness. Despite my immense love for my husband, I can't even be a mother. I'm always sick, discouraged, forlorn..."

"Come now!" ventured Ernesto, striving to find an optimistic way out for her. "Don't blame yourself. If not for you, the fellow would have done the same thing for some other reason. The suicidal impulse, as much as the criminal one..."

His voice trailed off again as if deep down he was repressing certain memories that his words were bringing to mind; however, giving the impression that he had gotten them under control, he continued:

"These are mysteries of the soul. Maybe they're the tip of mental diseases that the spirit has been harboring for a long time. Suicide and crime should be feared by all of us because they are acts of insanity resulting from deep processes of mental erosion."

"You're trying to make me feel better with your kindness of heart," said Evelina thoughtfully. "You've probably never experienced such an acute problem troubling your conscience."

"What? Me?" stuttered Fantini, unnerved. "Don't remind me of my past, for God's sake! I've made so many mistakes, suffered so many disappointments!"

And trying to skirt the issue without avoiding it, Ernesto forced a smile with the skill of mature persons who know how to use certain facial expressions for certain psychological effects, adding:

"Weren't you able to forget the suicide with the help of the confessionary? Didn't your spiritual counselor soothe your sensitive, kind heart?"

"Like I said, I've always found confessing my minor offences to be a sort of moral vaccine against bigger ones; but in this case I wasn't able to find the peace of mind I was looking for ... I believe that if I hadn't been divided between the two men for such a long time, I could have prevented the disaster. All I have to do is think of the unfortunate Tulio and the picture of his death flashes back into my mind, and with it comes the guilt."

"You shouldn't be so distraught. You're still very young. Just like the hand that gradually becomes calloused working in the field, sensitivity hardens by means of life's sufferings. Of course, if we survive the leap we are about to take for our health, we will witness many suicides, disappointments and calamities to come."

Mrs. Serpa thought for a few moments, and as if she were trying to use the opportunity to soothe her inner wounds, she asked pointedly:

"You've been studying the science of the soul. Do you really believe we will see our loved ones again after we die?"

Fantini answered obligingly:

"I don't know why, but your question reminds me of a quote by Shakespeare: "The miserable have no other medicine but only hope."[3] I have good reason to believe we will see each other again after we leave this world; however, I realize that my present precarious health may be the setting agent for such a conviction. Have you ever noticed that ideas and words are the offspring of circumstances? Imagine if you and I had found ourselves in the fullness of our physical strength, healthy and attractive, meeting at a social event – a ball, for instance ... Any thoughts about the matters that have now brought us together would be immediately banished from our minds."

"How true."

"The disease that afflicts us gives us the right to intertwine new resources and new interpretations concerning life and death, and in the realm of the new ideas lying before us, I believe that life does not end at the grave. We are forced to remember the old cliché in romantic novels: "Romance ends but life goes on..." The envelope of flesh will topple over, spent; the spirit, however, will carry on, always forward!"

"Do you ever think of who you'd like to see again in the *other life*?"

He smiled enigmatically and mocked:

"I can think of somebody I'd rather not!"

"I don't get the pun. Nonetheless, I feel comforted with your certainty about the future."

"You mustn't and shouldn't lose your trust in the future. Remember that, above all else, you are a Christian, a disciple of a Master who rose from the grave on the third day after his death."

Mrs. Serpa didn't smile. She gazed beyond at the rosy clouds reflecting the setting sun, realizing, perhaps, that she had been shaken to the depths of her faith by that unexpected comment.

---

[3] Shakespeare, *Measure for Measure* – Tr.

After a long pause, she looked at Ernesto again and prepared to say goodbye:

"Well, Mr. Fantini, if there is *another life* after this one, and if it is God's will for us to go through the *great change* before long, I think we shall meet again and be good friends *there...*"

"And why not? If I happen to foresee the end of my body, I shall keep the positive thought of our meeting firmly in my mind."

"Me too."

"When are you going back to Sao Paulo?"

"Tomorrow morning."

"Has your surgery been scheduled yet?"

"My husband will decide that with the doctor, but I think I shall face it next week. What about you?"

"I'm not sure, but I think it's only a matter of days. I don't want to postpone the surgery. Would you perchance give me the name of your hospital?"

Evelina thought and thought ... and concluded:

"Mr. Fantini, we're both suffering from the same rare and treacherous disease. Isn't that reason enough for us to feel close to each other? Let's await the future without anxiety. If we manage to pull through the ordeal, I'm sure God will grant us another meeting while still here on earth. But if death does come, our friendship in the *other world* will also be subject to the designs of Providence."

Ernesto smiled at her remark and both returned to the hotel walking slowly in heartfelt silence.

4
Renewal

Evelina only remembered the comforting presence of Ernesto, the friend she barely knew, after Caio Serpa, her husband, left her in that spacious hospital room on the eve of her surgery. She was there now, mulling over strange thoughts.

She was too young and was almost too sure of her recovery to dwell on any gloomy outlook. Nevertheless, as she lay there alone while waiting for the nurse, Fantini's assertions crossed her mind, stoking her imagination.

Yes, she was distressed to realize, she was about to face a serious risk. Perhaps she would not return to her family ... If she did die, where would she go? When she was a little girl, she trustingly believed in predestined places of either happiness or suffering, according to what the old Catholic theology said about people's situation after death. Now, however, with science exploring the cosmic immensity, she was intelligent enough to realize how tactful her aging priest had been in speaking with her about the indispensable renewals being imposed on the religious realm. From him, her learned and kind friend, she had learned to keep an unwavering trust in God, in the divine apostolate of Jesus Christ and the ineffable ministry of the saints. However, she had decided to set aside for reconsideration all statements of human authority regarding the things and workings of Divine Providence. The idea of death arose in her mind even more forcefully, but Evelina resisted it. She wanted health, physical well-being. She longed to recover, to live. Suddenly, she began to think about her problems at home. She was obviously going through a terrible phase in her marriage. Nevertheless, she had reason to believe that things could be happily worked out. She believed she was in her prime as a woman; the only thing she lacked was a return to physical health. Once she had recovered, she would apply herself in getting *the other woman* out of the picture. She would change her love interaction with her husband. She was so intent on making it better that her husband would of course return her love without her having to resort to acrimony or argument. More than that, she felt she was useful. She should get her life back; fight for it at any price. She should feel useful not only to her family but also to less fortunate people. Of course, she could fight poverty wherever poverty could be found ...

Thinking about the needy touched her ... How many were right there nearby, isolated from each other only by walls? Why hadn't she ever thought of that before?

She had spent her life as a satellite orbiting three people: her husband, mother and stepfather ...Why not take back her energies, renew herself, live? Yes, she would refuse any thought about the phenomena of death and would concentrate all the strength she was capable of on reestablishing herself physically.

She had read many psychologists and had learned the importance of a mental frame of mind. She desired to be healed.

She would say it as many times as possible with all the emotional power she could muster, choosing words loaded with energy that would define the states of her soul more clearly.

"Ah!" she said to herself, "in that sense, I should also pray!"

Upon formulating this idea, she was suddenly met with a picture of the crucified Jesus hanging on the wall. She contemplated the sublime face the artist had shaped with deep sentiment, and crossing herself, she said, more with her heart than with her lips:

"Lord, have mercy on me!"

But as she gazed on that head crowned with thorns, and those hands nailed to the cross of sacrifice, it seemed that Christ wished to be remembered by people in that depiction of pain so that they would be reminded of the inexorability of death.

An intense moral jolt shook her nervous system; she no longer knew whether she should choose to live or to die. Hiding her face in her hands, she knelt down humbly in front of the delicate painting and wept copiously.

Somebody spoke to her gently:

"Why are you crying, ma'am?'

An attentive nurse had come to prepare her for surgery.

Evelina stood up, wiped her tears and smiled:

"I'm sorry."

"No, I'm the one who has disturbed you, Mrs. Serpa," apologized the young woman. "Forgive me for interrupting your prayers, but we need to get ready. Also, your husband is waiting to see you."

The patient obeyed and left the room for a few minutes, returning soon thereafter.

Her husband was waiting for her, reading the daily paper.

"So," he joked, pretending to sound good-humored, "today, the *beauty parlor;* tomorrow, the return to health."

Caio Serpa's voice displayed energy and tenderness at the same time. He was a young lawyer, but, experienced in public relations, he exhibited studied though pleasant manners. A true representative of the social elite, not a hair was out of place. However, one could say that, down deep, the young lawyer was hiding, trying hard not to reveal the enigmatic aspects of his soul. His physical appearance didn't match what he was feeling inside. The varnish of academia couldn't completely erase the animalistic remainders, still present in the very human and natural character of the inhabitants of this earth. Furthermore, to our spirit perception, he displayed somber preoccupations.

After his first, tender words, he approached his wife and kissed her hair.

She didn't try to hide her joy and their conversation brimmed with affection.

Evelina reiterated the certainty that she would recover soon, while Caio spoke about the in-laws. On their small farm in the south, they would be awaiting the good news about the surgery and would be arriving for a visit at the first opportunity. They wouldn't come immediately so as not to seem overly concerned. They wanted to give their beloved daughter the impression that they were totally confident about the course of her treatment.

And Caio talked about much more.

He had consulted with his doctor friends. He had researched interesting studies regarding adrenal gland surgery. Concerning Evelina's particular case, the surgeon was optimistic. What else could they hope for now but success with God's blessings?

She was delighted to hear the expression "God's blessings." Was something new stirring in that beloved thirty-year-old atheist? she asked herself. Caio looked different, more attentive. Being simple at heart, she didn't realize he was play acting. Caio was making it all up. Neither the family doctor nor the surgeon had guaranteed anything more than an exploratory surgery with little hope of success. Even the cardiologist had almost advised against the operation, and had agreed to it only because the young woman was about to die anyway. Why say no to a procedure that might save her life? Her husband knew the list of concerns; however, at that moment, he exhibited a comforting outlook and lied out of compassion when commenting on the tests that only confirmed the forewarnings regarding the severity of the situation.

Caio spent the night at the hospital as a companion of the patient. He helped the nurse on night duty to administer Evelina's pre-anesthesia tranquilizers. He surrounded the patient with loving care as if she were a child and he a caring father.

The following day after the surgery, however, Caio was called in to see the surgeon; he blanched white when he received the prognosis. According to the resources of human science, Evelina had only a few more days to live. As her husband, he should take all the steps he deemed necessary to make her as comfortable as possible.

The doctor summed up his opinion in only one sentence:

"She looks like a rose completely eaten away by malignant agents."

Although he wanted to, he no longer heard the learned remarks regarding neoplasms, secondary foci, metastases and tumors that return after excision. Caio felt petrified. Tears streamed down his face.

At the end of the display of sympathy and human tenderness with which he was comforted by the surgeon, he ran to be with his prostrate companion. And for several days and nights of patience and worry, he acted as her brother, father, tutor and friend.

At his behest, his in-laws came to console their daughter during her final days. Brigida, her mother, and Amancio Terra, her stepfather, owners of a prosperous farm in the south of Sao Paulo state, arrived completely forlorn, but they tried to find words of optimism while holding back their tears.

Supported by the web of her family's devotion, Evelina seemed to improve and returned to her domestic world. There, she was pampered as she had not been for quite some time, while at the same time suffering the periodic choking spells that left her exhausted.

Despite her perilous condition, she believed the uplifting opinions of her family and friends.

She believed it would pass, that it was only the aftermath of the kind of surgery she had gone through. She should be confident and pray faithfully.

After two weeks of alternating calm and relapse, she had six days of continuous well-being.

Despite being extremely thin and weak, she left her bed for a lounge chair; she ate almost normally and talked peaceably. She also enjoyed religious comfort – compliments of a devoted priest – and in the evening she asked her stepfather to read her something joyful and pleasant for a few minutes.

Late in the afternoon on the fifth day of this hopeful outlook, Evelina made a surprising request.

Would it be possible for Caio to take her to their favorite place when they were engaged?"

"Morumbi[4] at night?" asked her puzzled mother.

Evelina explained her request. She wanted to see the sparkling lights of the city from a distance. She missed the starry sky.

Caio phoned the doctor and the doctor gave his permission.

---

[4] At the time the book was written, Morumbi was a green tract of land near the center of Sao Paulo. Today, it is an upscale residential area. – Tr.

Eager to please her once more, her husband pulled the car out of the garage, and carrying her in his arms as if she were a little girl, he sat her comfortably beside him; declining his in-laws' company, they set out.

The patient was enthralled. She saw the busy streets once again and afterwards the scenery of Morumbi and its nature-filled surroundings.

Listening to her talk enthusiastically, Caio was moved. It was as if she were his beloved once more, the woman he had loved passionately years before. He felt remorse at remembering his conjugal infidelity. He wanted to ask for her forgiveness, to confess, but realized that this was not the right time.

He stopped the car and looked at her. Evelina seemed ethereal; her eyes shone in the moonlight and her head moved as if haloed with light...

Caio took her in his strong arms with the longing of someone who wanted to seize a treasure and protect it ... In an irresistible rapture of love, he kissed her again and again, until he felt her cool face moistened with hot tears.

Evelina was weeping with joy.

When she felt free of those beloved arms, she bent her head slightly to linger on the sight of the sky, which now looked like a gigantic field decorated with flowers of silver and fire.

She held his hand tightly and asked:

"Caio, do you believe we will meet again after we die?"

He didn't answer, started the engine, urged her to change the subject, lovingly told her that she was forbidden from discussing what he regarded as *sad things*, and they headed back.

On the way home, Evelina remembered how easy it had been to talk to Ernesto Fantini, the unexpected friend at the resort. She couldn't explain why, but she missed his gentle and pleasant presence. She was thirsty for spiritual conversation. She desired to talk about the secrets of eternal life and to listen to someone on the same topic and the same wavelength. At that moment, however, Caio gave her the impression of a strange violin that no longer responded to the strings of the bow. Her sublime emotions died in her chest for want of expansion and response. For that reason, she preferred to simply listen to her husband, to bless him and do as he wished.

One more peaceful day and then Evelina woke up in a crisis. Getting worse and worse despite the painkillers, the young Mrs. Serpa had spent her last night in the world.

Before the profound sorrow of her husband and parents, who had done everything they could to keep her alive, Evelina, exhausted, closed the eyes of her physical body in final deliverance, just as the stars were fading in the new dawn.

5
Reunion

Evelina woke up in a spacious bedroom with two windows that allowed her to see the sky.

She had awakened from a heavy sleep, she thought.

She tried to get her bearings and appraise her situation.

How had she fallen into this amnesia, from which she was only now returning to consciousness?

Making a great effort, she began to slowly remember ... First, an indescribable nightmare had troubled her as she had started to go to sleep. Most probably she must have suffered a fainting spell. She saw herself moving through an exotic world of images that forced her to regress down the pathway of her memories. She had recapitulated – she didn't know how – all the phases of her short life. She had gone back in time. She reconstructed all the days she had lived, back to the point of seeing her father brought home dead when she was only two years old. In this movie, which the hidden energies of her mind had shown to her in the innermost corners of her being, she had heard once more her mother's screams and saw the stunned neighbors, unable to understand the tragedy that had struck her home.

Next, she remembered feeling a huge jolt.

It was as if something had been untied in her brain and then she saw herself floating over her own sleeping body.

Soon thereafter, an overpowering sleep had taken over.

That was all she remembered.

How many hours had she lingered in that unexpected languor? Could it be that, as the result of some miraculous treatment, she was regaining consciousness after having collapsed? Why didn't she see anyone near her bed, someone from the family to explain what had happened?

She tried to sit up and succeeded without any difficulty.

She inspected the surroundings and concluded that they had taken her to another room. From what she could gather, after fainting she had been taken back to the hospital and was now in a spacious room of a relaxing light green color.

On a nearby table she saw roses that called her attention to their fragrance.

Delicate curtains swayed gently to the rhythm of the breeze that came in through unusual Venetian blinds made of a substance similar to crystal covered with an emerald-like material.

Everywhere simplicity and purpose, comfort and lightness.

Evelina yawned, raised her arms and did not feel any pain.

She had finally been healed, she thought happily.

She knew the presence of health and she felt it within her. No suffering, no restrictions.

If she felt anything at all unpleasant, it was that sure sign of organic health: she was starving.

Where was her husband? Her parents?

She wanted to shout out her happiness and tell them she was healed. She longed to tell them that all their sacrifices on her behalf had not been in vain. Inwardly, she thanked God for the gift of her recovery and very much wanted to extend her joyous gratitude to her loved ones.

She could no longer contain her joy-filled heart and reached for the buzzer beside her. She pressed the button and a woman with a sweet, pretty face entered, greeting her with loving care.

Evelina readily accepted the unknown woman's assistance.

"Nurse," she asked the newcomer, "would you please call my husband?"

"I have instructions to first inform the doctor that you are better."

Mrs. Serpa agreed but insisted that she felt the need to share her joy with her family.

"I understand," replied the woman kindly.

"I'm anxious to talk to someone," added the convalescent eagerly. "What's your name?"

"Call me Sister Isa."

"You must know who I am. My name is Evelina Serpa and you must have my chart..."

"Yes."

"Sister Isa, what happened to me? I feel fine, but in a strange way that I can't quite define."

"You've been through a *long surgery*. You must rest, recover."

Although spoken in a significant way, these words were not surprising. She knew she had been through surgery. She had gone through the painful removal of a tumor. She had returned home and had improved to the point where she had gone for a ride with her husband through the roads of Morumbi. And yet, she found herself once more in the hospital without knowing why.

While silently mulling this, she missed seeing the nurse press a grey button on the wall, calling the doctor on duty.

In a couple minutes, a man dressed in white calmly entered the room.

He greeted the patient, examined her and smiled, satisfied.

"Doctor..." Evelina started to say, anxious to explain herself.

She wanted some information. She wanted to know how and when she could see her husband and parents.

Wouldn't it be fair to give her loved ones the news of her success at this hospital?

The doctor listened to her calmly and asked her to be patient. She would see her family, but first she needed to get readjusted.

With kind gestures, as if putting a child at ease, he explained:

"You are better now, much better; however, you are still under strict watch regarding your mental state. If you tune into anything capable of inducing you to actively remember the disease you suffered, all the symptoms will most likely reappear. Think about that. It wouldn't be advisable to meet your family right now."

And with an even more understanding look, he added:

"Please cooperate."

Evelina listened to his explanation with tear-filled eyes, but accepted it without resistance.

After all, she concluded, she should be grateful to those who had granted her the blessing of her recovery. She didn't have the right to interfere with measures she couldn't understand. Guessing that the doctor was about to leave, she asked humbly if she was allowed to read, and if so, she wondered if the hospital could lend her a book containing Christ's teachings. Moved by her request, the doctor remembered the New Testament, and in just a few moments the nurse brought one to her.

Alone again, Evelina started to read the Sermon on the Mount; however, the doctor's advice kept coming insistently back to her mind ... If she had recovered – as she seemed to have – why could simple memories compel the return of the suffering she found herself to be free of? Why? She felt possessed of an indescribable euphoria. A delightful sensation of lightness kept her in a joyous mood, one she had never felt in her entire life.

Could these indicators of bodily health vanish so easily?

She put the book aside and became engulfed in more thoughts ... What would happen if she did intensely visualize Caio and her parents there with her? What if she did concentrate her thoughts on all the pain she had left behind?

Unfortunately, she yielded to such exercises and in just a few minutes the crisis was full blown, quickly overpowering her body. Her hands and feet became icy cold, while it seemed that a fire burned inside her, the dyspnea[5] suffocating her chest. With these symptoms unleashed, Evelina tried to fight back, to concentrate on health instead of disease; but it was too late. Suffering overpowered her strength and she writhed in the agony she thought she had left behind for good.

Stunned, she pressed the buzzer and the helpful nurse made every effort to assist her.

The doctor returned and gave her some sedatives.

Neither the doctor nor the nurse reproached her in the least, but Evelina could see in their eyes that they knew exactly what had happened. In their silence they let her know that they were aware of her stubbornness, and that, obviously not heeding their warnings, she had wanted to find out for herself what an inappropriate mentalization would do.

His kindness notwithstanding, the doctor was very firm.

---

[5] **Dyspnea:** Difficult or labored breathing; shortness of breath. http://www.medterms.com/script/main/art.asp?articlekey=3145 – Tr.

After giving Mrs. Serpa a tranquilizing injection in a certain area of her head, he gave strict instructions to the nurse, prescribing special measures for her to sleep. It was advisable to use anesthetics to enable her to rest longer. The patient could not and should not surrender to fixated ideas, lest she return to unnecessary suffering.

Evelina registered his words as she drifted off. She then lost herself in a heavy sleep. She awakened several hours later, aware of the fact that she had to take care to avoid another panic-filled bout. Showing a desire to eat, she was immediately served some hot, comforting broth that tasted like a delicious nectar.

She recovered and was wide awake. She realized she was under a type of treatment whose effectiveness and power she couldn't underestimate.

After a week of complete rest and enjoying only the reading materials chosen by those in charge of her, she began to walk around the room.

When she had stood up again, she noticed unmistakable differences in herself. Her feet seemed lighter, as if she had lost a lot of weight; what is more, in her mind ideas were born in torrents, strong and beautiful, almost materializing themselves before her eyes.

On an afternoon when she felt more encouraged to move around naturally, she walked toward the window overlooking an enormous courtyard, and from the third floor where she was staying, she saw dozens of people conversing happily. Several of them were sitting around a beautiful fountain in the middle of a huge flower garden.

That peaceful gathering attracted her.

She was eager for social contact, restrained as she was by austere discipline. Thus, she asked the nurse if she was allowed to go down and maybe talk to someone. After all, she suggested optimistically, a hospital is like a ship where individuals are interested in and lend a helping hand to each other.

The nurse laughed and held her by the arm to go down to the garden.

Yes, she could enjoy herself there. The air would do her good and she might also make a new friend.

Left on her own, she gazed longingly at the faces around her. It seemed as if she were in the midst of a huge family, kindred souls, but almost all of them strangers to each other, like at a resort.

Everyone there seemed to be convalescing, and one could easily discern the vestiges of the infirmities they had managed to defeat.

Evelina was deciding what would be the best way to approach someone when she saw a man not far away looking at her in obvious astonishment. Oh, my goodness! Wasn't that gentleman Ernesto Fantini, the new friend from the hot springs? Her heart beat faster and she extended both arms in his direction, giving him the certainty that she had been expecting him with all her soul.

Fantini – it was in fact him – got out of the armchair and walked quickly toward her.

"Evelina! ... Dona Evelina! ... Is it really you?"

"Yes, it's me!" answered the young woman, crying with joy.

The newcomer could not ignore the emotion of that unforgettable moment. Tears ran down her serious, kind face; embarrassed, she sought to dry her tears while trying to smile.

6
Fraternal Understanding

"How long have you been here?"

"Well actually, I don't know for sure," replied Ernesto, eager to talk.

And he continued:

"I've been thinking a lot about our chat in Poços de Caldas and I've been hoping to see you again."

"How very kind!"

Evelina confided in him about how confused she was feeling. She had woken up in this completely unfamiliar hospital; it was obviously her family's decision. The only thing she remembered clearly was fainting after one of the severest spells she had ever had.

And smiling, she remarked that she had actually had the impression that she was *dying...*

How long had she been unconscious? She had no idea.

She had regained her senses only after a heavy, dreamless sleep up there in her room on the third floor.

Since then, she had been puzzled by the mystery involving the hospital administration's handling of her case because she had not even been given permission to call her husband.

Fantini listened to her closely without saying a word.

Around them, people were sitting or walking easily about, or reading or chatting here and there.

The extremely diaphanous atmosphere was delightfully scented with the fragrance of roses, forget-me-nots, jasmines, carnations, begonias and other flowers amid trees that looked like almonds, ficuses and magnolias.

As Evelina elaborated, Fantini listened to her attentively, nodding in agreement with a strange glow in his eyes.

He confessed that he too was troubled. He told her he also had experienced a strange release from himself, except that in his case it happened immediately after the surgery as he was being taken back to bed, from what he could remember. Like Mrs. Serpa, he had experienced the same past-memory phenomenon in which he had suddenly been transported back into the past, starting with his astonishment about what was happening at the moment and ending with the first days of his childhood.

After that, he had slept soundly.

Incapable of explaining how long, exactly, he had been unconscious, he had woken up in this hospital ten days ago.

He too was puzzled by the rules of the institution because he had not been able to make the least contact with his wife or daughter, to whom he had said goodbye in the hospital room a few hours before being taken to surgery.

These circumstances filled him with anxiety.

She, Evelina, had experienced an enigmatic fainting spell while with her loved ones at home, whereas he had left his family amid agonizing expectations and had been denied any means of communicating with them. He realized that this hospital was not the same one in which he had undergone the surgery – he even doubted that he was still in Sao Paulo. The sky looked a bit different at night, and the swimming pool he had been using contained highly purified water, although it was understandable that a hospital would have special filters and equipment to treat ordinary water.

Ernesto finished his story and asked:

"Have you been to the hot springs yet?"

"Not yet."

"You'll understand my amazement when you do."

"What makes you think I'll be going there?" asked Evelina with the playful tone of someone who felt a bit more comfortable.

"You will. I've heard that hydrotherapy is compulsory here."

Fantini smiled meaningfully and stated, each word loaded with concern:

"Do you know what seems more likely? I suspect that our families had us committed to a psychiatric institution. I don't know a thing about medicine, but I have a sneaking suspicion that our adrenal gland problems have affected our minds. Maybe we have gone mad and are on the verge of complete mental alienation; segregating us might have been the recommended course of action."

"What makes you think so?" asked Evelina, very pale.

"Dona Evelina..."

"Just call me Evelina. I insist that we be friends – actually, more like brother and sister."

"Sounds good," agreed Fantini.

And he continued:

"Evelina, wait till you see the odd devices they use to apply rays to our heads before the medicinal bath. And believe me: all the patients have displayed gradual improvement. Since I went to the bath for the first time the day before yesterday, I have felt more lucid and lighter, much lighter."

"Haven't you felt more mentally balanced since you woke up?"

"Not really. I was so anxious for a word from my family that I once again fell into a severe crisis. All I had to do was remember my wife and daughter, along with the operation, and I immediately felt the terrible oppression in my chest and passed out from the pain."

Evelina remembered her own experience, but kept silent. She was becoming ever more concerned.

"Judging from the careful way they have been responding to my questions," continued Fantini, "it seems they are trying to keep us in a state of calm and tranquility. I could accept the fact that we have gone through some sort of psychological trauma and that we are now trying to regain our stability, which we are doing little by little. I think our treatment is purely mental. Just yesterday, I began complaining again, asking to be allowed to communicate with my family. But do you know what the completely self-assured nurse on duty said to me?"

"What?"

"Brother Fantini, don't worry about it. Your family is well aware of your absence." "But, don't they want to talk to me? Or to phone me, at least?" I asked. And the nurse answered: "Your wife and your daughter know they cannot hope to see you at home in the near future." And because I insisted and demanded that something be done, the young woman replied: "For the time being, that's all I can tell you."

"So what have you concluded from all this?"

"Unless I'm completely wrong, I think it's obvious that we have been mentally ill without knowing it," suggested Fantini, almost in good humor again, "and I'm certain that we are coming back very slowly from mental darkness to the normal state of consciousness. The doctors and nurses around here are completely right for trying to guard us against any type of concern with life on the outside. The smallest sign of affliction on the mental screen of our feelings at the moment – so I believe – could maybe do a lot of harm to our emotions and thoughts, much like what occurs with the small distortion that adversely affects the symmetry of electric waves."

"That's possible."

Both of them paused at length.

After some time deeply immersed in his inner world, Ernesto broke the silence:

"Evelina, before the terrible attack you mentioned earlier, did you talk to a priest? Did he tell you anything? Did he give you any advice?"

Evelina became frightened in light of the angst in his questions, and asked in return:

"Why? Why do you ask? Whenever I could, I would confess before passing out ... but why do you want to know? Are you joking?"

Fantini was not joking. His eyes revealed undisguised discomfort.

"Don't worry. I'm just asking," he said, tapping the fingers of his left hand on the stool in front of him. "Considering the dangerous episodes we have both been through, any kind of help would be welcome ... I remembered that you are a religious person and that I am still a man without faith..."

Ernesto had not yet finished his sentence when a young woman in a group of three people who were strolling not far away collapsed on the ground as if suddenly taken with a violent attack of hysteria, crying out in obvious mental agony:

"No! ... I can't stand it anymore! ... I want my home, my family! ... My mother! ... Where's my mother? Open the doors! ...

Criminals! Who here's brave enough to help me pull down these walls?! Cops! Call the cops!"

It was obviously a case of madness, but there was so much suffering in that voice that those sitting nearby stood up in fright.

A woman radiating patience and goodness, displaying on her uniform the badge of one of the hospital's nurses, cleared a path through the onlookers who had begun to gather around. She held the distraught girl in her arms like a mother, and without the slightest trace of reprimand, picked her up, saying with the utmost kindness:

"My child, who told you that you won't be able to go home? That you won't see your mother again? Our doors are always open ... Come with me!"

"Ah! Sister," sighed the girl, instantly assured by those kind strong hands holding her, "forgive me! ... Forgive me! I have no reason to complain, but I miss my mother, my home! How long have I been here without seeing any of my family? I know I'm ill and am receiving the gift of being healed, but why haven't I gotten any news?!"

The nurse listened to her calmly and promised only:

"You will."

Then, putting her caring arm around the girl's shoulders, she finished:

"But now, we must rest!"

Like someone who had found in her benefactor some memory of the maternal warmth she missed so much, the girl rested her blond head on the nurse's chest and they left, the girl still sobbing.

Evelina and Ernesto had run to help the girl and witnessed the scene with a mixture of affliction and anguish.

Both of them were eager for an explanation.

What were they to gather from the tearful plea of the child suffering from being away from home? What kind of hospital was this? An emergency unit for the mentally disturbed? An institution for the recovery of amnesiacs?

On an impulse of curiosity she could no longer control, Evelina approached a nice looking woman who had watched the scene attentively, and whose gray hair reminded her of her mother's. She asked discreetly:

"Excuse me, ma'am. We've never met, but our shared affliction has brought us together. Could you tell us something about that poor disturbed girl?"

"Who? Me?" asked the woman.

And she stated:

"My dear, I know practically nothing about other people's lives here."

"But please listen to me. Do you know where we are? What hospital this is?"

The woman got closer to Evelina, who, in turn, stepped back toward Fantini, and whispered:

"You don't know?"

In light of Mrs. Serpa's undisguised bewilderment, she directed a penetrating glance at Ernesto and repeated the question:

"And you?"

"We don't know a thing," stated Fantini politely.

"Well, someone told me that we are all dead, that we are no longer living on the earth."

Fantini took a handkerchief from his pocket in order to wipe the sweat that began to run abundantly down his forehead, while Evelina staggered, ready to pass out.

The stranger supported her, and looking very worried, suggested:

"My dear, compose yourself! We live under strict discipline here. If you show any trace of weakness or rebelliousness, I don't know when you'll be able to come back to this courtyard."

"Let's sit down," suggested Ernesto.

He offered Evelina his arm, and helped by the woman, they managed to lead her to a nearby bench in a nook under a large ficus, where they sat down to rest for a while.

7
Alzira Provides Information

"Let's talk," said their new friend.

Afraid that someone might be watching, she did her best not to attract any attention. She made every effort to look natural, concerned that someone might have noticed Mrs. Serpa's reaction.

Fantini understood and did his best to do likewise.

Making an effort to ignore the pallor on Mrs. Serpa's face, the woman introduced herself with apparent composure:

"My name is Alzira Campos and I live in Sao Paulo."

She gave them her address, talked about her family, described her neighborhood and added:

"When I fell at home, they brought me unconscious to this hospital, and as far as I can tell, I have been here for nearly two months waiting to be released."

Ernesto and Alzira struck up a conversation, while Evelina slowly regained her composure.

"Feeling better?"

"A lot."

"Mrs. Campos, have you talked to anybody with authority who might be able to answer your questions about what's in store for us?"

"Yes; sister Leticia, who has assisted me from the start with the medicinal baths, told me the day before yesterday that the day is coming when I'll be able to decide whether I want to stay here or not."

"What do you think she meant by *to stay here or not?*"

"Actually, knowing how much I want to go home, you can imagine how upset I was."

"You didn't ask her anything else?"

"I did; I begged for more details. But the only thing she kindly said was: 'You'll understand better later.'"

"Dona Alzira," whispered Ernesto firmly, "Don't you think we are in a mental hospital, an insane asylum?"

Alzira glanced around like a patient afraid of vigilant guards and opined:

"If we're going to discuss serious matters, we shouldn't exclude our friend Evelina. She could help speed up her own recovery. Let's order something for her to drink."

Alzira pressed a small button on the table and a young attendant appeared, readily asking how he might be useful.

Alzira ordered juice for three.

"What flavor?"

"Apple."

In a few moments he came back with a sapphire-blue tray bearing three glasses containing an aromatic pinkish liquid.

"In my opinion, this is the best beverage I've found here so far. It seems to have calming properties," said Alzira when they were alone again.

Evelina eagerly took a sip. It gave her the impression of being some sort of nectar, more vaporous than liquid.

The unexpected blend renewed her strength and regrouped her thoughts.

"I feel better," she said right away. "Thank God!"

Alzira smiled, showing her willingness to continue the conversation and to give her new friends all the information she could.

Fantini said in a low voice:

"Back to the subject. Don't you suspect we are undergoing some sort of specialized mental treatment?"

"At first," clarified Alzira, "I thought so. Note, however, that our thoughts are clearer and our minds are lighter. The ideas flow so quickly and spontaneously that they seem to materialize right in front of us. I agree that we are in a different spiritual state than the one we were in before we got here, but even so, I don't think this is an insane asylum. It's obvious that we are surrounded by a busy city life. There are homes, schools, institutions, places of worship, industries, vehicles, public entertainment..."

"What?" exclaimed Evelina and Ernesto at the same time.

"It's just as I'm telling you. This is a relatively large city of no less than a hundred thousand, and according to what I've heard, extremely well-run."

"Have you ever managed to spend any time outside? Have you ever left the premises?" asked Ernesto, full of curiosity.

"Yes, last week I got permission to go with two friends on a visit to a family I had never met before. So far, that has been the only time I've been away from the hospital. I can tell you the trip was really delightful, despite my astonishment at the end of it."

"What and who did you see?" probed Ernesto.

"You don't need to concern yourself with it for now; you'll get to know everything at the right time. The city is beautiful. It's a sort of valley of buildings that seem to be made of jade, crystal and lapis-lazuli; unusual architecture, charming squares decorated with gardens. Believe me, I walked completely enchanted street after street. Brother Nicomedes, the house's owner, received us very kindly. He introduced me to his daughter Corina, a beautiful girl I was immediately drawn to. A close friend to one of the two young women I was with, and with whom she was going to discuss some work matters, Corina expressed the festive jubilation of their household in talking with us about its joys. She showed us new chandeliers, paintings and magnificent vases. Everything was happening in a crescendo of delightful surprises until ... the jolt that hit me at the core. We were on the terrace admiring a hanging jasmine garden when we heard 'Dreams of love' by Liszt being played on the piano. Corina told us her father played superbly. I was touched so deeply that I expressed my desire to listen up close. Our hostess immediately took us to the music room. It was dazzling. Brother Nicomedes was immersed in a world of profound joy that radiated from within him in the form of melodies, remarkable pieces of music one after another. At a certain moment I said, 'He seems immersed in prolonged ecstasy; he plays as if he were praying,' to which his daughter responded, 'Yes, we are indeed very happy. We have been told that my mother is arriving this week.' 'Has she been traveling?' I asked. To which the girl replied quite naturally, 'My mother is coming from earth.' When I heard that I felt a terrible jolt, as if I had just been hit in the chest. I couldn't breathe and before I knew it I was overcome by a terrible bout of chest oppression. The mere idea that we were in a place away from the world I had always known sent me back into the painful angina that I had not felt for a long time. Without saying a word, Corina understood and brought me a tranquilizer. From what I could tell, my state of anguish affected the whole place, because our host stopped abruptly in the middle of a beautiful nocturne. I was about to pass out. The small group gathered around me and took me out into the open air. They sat me in a curious chair made of stone similar to marble. I touched the back of it, and verifying the solidity of the matter under my hands, I began to settle down ... Then I looked at the sky and saw the full moon shining with such beauty that I calmed down completely. I realized how senseless my fright had been, and I said to myself, Why couldn't there be a city, town, village or some other place called *Earth?* The scenery that surrounded me was undoubtedly some corner of the world ... That explained it; Nicomedes' wife was coming from some unknown town ... I was digesting my conclusions when the head of the household asked compassionately, 'How long has our sister Alzira been here?' 'A little over two months,' answered one of my care-givers. Nothing else was said about me. The visit was over. On the way back to the hospital, the women whom I had gone with, and who are, by the way, two excellent nurses, didn't make the slightest reference to my attack."

"Haven't you exchanged ideas with anyone else?" asked Fantini, very interested.

"Only during the baths do I listen to one or more of the people there. Each one of them has the same questions ... Most of them believe we are experiencing a different type of life."

"But none of them are absolutely sure?" interrupted Mrs. Serpa.

"Only Mrs. Tamburini is completely convinced that we are no longer in the earthly realm. She told me she has been attending sessions here in the hospital having to do with studies on magnetism. She has undergone tests that confirm that she no longer has a physical body. I listened to her closely. She ended up inviting me to a few experiments; I thanked her kindly but didn't accept. Such tales about *clairvoyance and reincarnation* don't jibe with my Catholic faith ..."

"Ah! So you're Catholic?" interrupted Evelina.

"Oh, yes!"

"Well, since we seem to be living in a big city, aren't there any priests here?"

"Yes, there are."

"Have you talked to any of them yet?"

"I've been invited to a church and I'll go as soon as I get permission. However, I must tell you that, according to reliable information, the priests are a lot different."

"How so?"

"They say the priests are also doctors, teachers, scientists and workers, and they're not limited to matters of faith. They render effective and positive spiritual help in the name of Jesus."

Fantini noticed that the courtyard was emptying out.

All the patients were leaving.

Their new friend Alzira suggested they meet again later and said goodbye. Soon afterward, Ernesto and Evelina also returned to their rooms in hopes of seeing each other again the next day.

8
An Instructive Meeting

Ernesto Fantini and Mrs. Serpa enjoyed hours and hours of comforting friendship in the courtyard engaged in interesting conversation.

More than two weeks had passed since their first meeting. Evelina, as much as her friend, had become accustomed to the therapeutic baths, and both had gotten in touch with Mrs. Tamburini, whom Alzira regarded as the most knowledgeable person she had met there. This helpful woman had promised to take them as soon as possible to the Institute of Sciences of the Spirit, which functioned right there in a corner of the big garden.

Without a doubt, the two of them thought Mrs. Tamburini's explanations were the most clarifying they had heard so far. In their almost daily tête-à-têtes, she asked them to reflect more deeply on matter, which gathers itself in various degrees, and a broader study of the mind's perceptions, which vary according to the principles of relativity. On other occasions, she asked that they observe their own extreme lightness, the agility of their new, subtle body, and the peculiar way they expressed their thoughts as if the ideas gushed from their minds in the form of images way beyond their usual capabilities; that they also examine, in that new sphere of life, the phenomenon of telepathic communication, considered an ordinary occurrence there, although spoken language was also used. All that was needed was a high degree of affinity between individuals for them to understand each other perfectly about the most complex subjects, using a minimum number of words.

They happily listened to the judicious observations of Mrs. Tamburini, who was fully convinced they were discarnate souls in some area of the spirit world. However, regardless of their respect for her, they couldn't accept what she said as the unquestionable truth.

Sitting on the grass near Fantini, who in turn was sitting on a small bench, Evelina started the conversation, thoughtfully appraising the situation:

"It's true that I feel lighter and lighter every day, and that because of it I feel like I'm losing control of myself. I've noticed that my feelings move up from my heart to my brain, like waters from a deep underground source pouring forth to the surface ... In my head I've noticed that emotions are transformed into thoughts that flow immediately to my lips in the form of words, departing from me like rivers that extend far beyond their birthplace to flow over the earth."

"Well put. You have defined my own state of mind precisely."

"But listen, Ernesto," advised Evelina, touching the trunk of a robust tree: "What do you see here?"

"A tree trunk."

"And over there in the nearest flower bed?"

"Carnations."

"Could this be the spirit world if matter and nature that are familiar to us are present everywhere?"

"I agree that neither of us has gotten a clear explanation regarding our present situation, and all this is absurd, maddening, but..."

"But?!"

"But we can't rush into affirming anything.

"Have you been influenced by Mrs. Tamburini's ideas?"

"Not so much. I draw my own conclusions."

"Listen, Ernesto. If we are dead to all our loved ones, why haven't any relatives who preceded us come looking for us yet? Our grandparents, for example, or close friends who have died?"

"Who says they haven't?"

"How can you say that?"

"Think about the elementary examples in our homes. A television receives images that we cannot see and transmits them with complete accuracy. A radio captures messages that we cannot hear in person and delivers them to us with perfect clarity. It's very likely that we are being watched and heard without our having yet awoken the precise faculty to hear and see on this plane."

"But Ernesto, what about the prayers? If we are spirits freed from the so-called physical body, someone must have remembered us in their prayers ... Your wife, your daughter, my parents, my husband..."

"We know neither the mechanism of spirit relationships, nor do we have any knowledge of the science of the soul. Who can say that we are not being supported by the power of the prayers of those we love or by others ... who still love us."

"What do you mean?"

"Have you received a hospital bill yet? To what and to whom do we owe the care and kindnesses we receive every day?

We don't buy our clothes, nor do we pay for the services we enjoy ... Have we ever asked any nurse the well-known question, 'Who's paying for all this?'"

"I have."

"And the answer?"

"Those who love you."

"And who might they be, in your opinion?"

"In my case, my husband and parents."

"I have my doubts. At first I thought we were recovering at a mental health institute; however, with every passing day we find ourselves at the highest level of awareness with regards to our reasoning. If we were in an asylum after a nervous breakdown, our recovery wouldn't be so quick."

The thread of their interesting conversation was suddenly broken.

Mrs. Tamburini approached them in a hurry to tell them that there was a spiritual instruction meeting set for that evening and that they had better get prepared.

In possession of the necessary authorization, they headed for the building at 7:00 p.m. with their friend, who introduced them to the mentor in charge, Brother Claudio.

They were received with a warm welcome in the room where twenty-three participants were seated, and they noticed an enormous globe, which would probably be used as a starting point for their invaluable learning experience.

The instructor began the meeting by stating that the lesson would be a conversational one, and that he was nothing more than their colleague in these studies, subject to the same errors, hypotheses, approximations and judgments regarding what he would say.

"What is the subject, professor?" asked a distinctive woman.

"Life on earth."

After having answered the question, the group's leader wove invaluable comments about the earthly orb's function in the cosmic economy, and then continued:

"Let us think this over, my friends. Considering how incomplete our current knowledge is, who here could claim to know everything there is to know based solely on his or her personal impressions? We are fully aware of the fact that the earth is a gigantic engine in space, carrying with it almost three billion[6] incarnated individuals through the avenues of the universe, but we don't yet know what kind of force is holding it up. All we know about this colossal body is that it follows an elliptical orbit around the sun at an average speed of 108,000 kilometers[7] per hour. While in certain regions of the planet people are standing with their heads toward the zenith, in other regions their heads are pointing downward toward the nadir, without anyone noticing it. Until recently, any person would have asserted that the dense matter of a landscape was formed of solid elements at rest; nowadays, however, any student knows that such impressions are imaginary, that matter everywhere consists of a mixture of electrons, protons, neutrons and deuterons, enveloped in energy and light. Every person lives in a body of which he or she is a tenant, and breathes and caters to the necessity of nourishment without any major effort on his or her part. How can one pose dogmatic affirmations concerning causes, processes, purification and the objective of our earthly existence by means of the limited resources of our five senses?"

After a long pause a gentleman ventured:

"Professor, in making such deductions you mean..."

"That life on earth must be interpreted as a special endeavor for the spirit. Each is born with a specific task, with

---

[6]   This book was written in 1968. – Tr.
[7]   Approximately 67,108 miles.

the potential of expanding into others that are ever more important. That is why it is not possible to deprive people of their religious principles without disastrous consequences. Science advances, unveiling the secrets of the universe, solving problems and looking for new challenges to its capacity for investigation. Faith, however, supports humans in the achievements and trials they are called to undergo. The spirit reincarnates in the physical world as many times as necessary for it to be useful, improve itself and become enlightened. And as it evolves, it begins to realize that physical life is an occupation or a mission to carry out, for which it will have to give an account in the end."

The speaker displayed such depth of knowledge in his exposition that very few remarks were heard.

Therefore, without deviating from the backdrop of the lecture, which was undoubtedly meant to prepare his listeners to peacefully accept their new spiritual state, he stated:

"If the Lord's laws are manifested clearly and magnanimously in all areas of the physical experience, could he possibly discard us after we cross the boundaries of death? We refer to the horrible annihilation of human lives when wars sweep over the face of the planet. However, what are we to conclude about those same human lives when they are methodically extinguished in times of peace? Could the Lord remain indifferent to our destinies anywhere in the universe? He, who provides the appropriate food for the child and for the adult, would he relegate the discarnate individual to abandonment, while the individual clothed in physical elements lives and acts in a sphere of action in which foresight and watch care offer the most beautiful displays of magnificence every day?"

No one there was able to probe the depths of the enigmatic nature of those statements. The listeners – at least most of them –

didn't realize that they were gently being prepared to accept their spiritual reality without being too troubled by it.

After a longer pause, while the instructor pointed out geographical positions on the globe, Evelina summoned up her courage and asked:

"Brother Claudio, does everybody experience the same things after death?"

"No. Each one of us is a world, complete in itself, and for this reason, after leaving the physical vehicle, each individual will experience emotions, places, persons, affinities and opportunities according to how they have performed their task, or better, the duties that were their responsibility during their existence on the earth. No one can know what they have not studied, nor retain qualities they have not acquired."

Claudio offered further comments rich in beauty and logic, and at the end of the brilliant lecture, Ernesto and Evelina felt comforted and happy, like travelers thirsty for values of the soul after having drunk from a fountain of light.

9
Brother Claudio

Having been referred by Mrs. Tamburini, who could not attend the meeting, Fantini and Mrs. Serpa stayed behind with Brother Claudio, who spoke with them personally when the meeting had ended.

He did not live there, he explained.

The Institute offered services throughout the building and required the entire premises. Claudio told them that he and his wife would be happy to have them over for a chat at their house, however. Since Mrs. Tamburini had referred him as an instructor who could give them information regarding issues of great importance to them, he made himself available to help them in any way he could, even though he knew that he might not be able to answer all their questions.

All this was said cordially in a moonlit corner of one of the institution's gardens, where small groups of students were scattered here and there.

The trio engaged in lively conversation around a table. The familiarity of the scene was so real that one might find it hard to believe that it wasn't happening down on the earth. Consequently, despite Ernesto's pensive look of uncertainty and anxiety, Evelina was completely convinced that she was in a regular corner of the world she knew so well.

"I understand you want to know a bit more about your new residence," said Brother Claudio serenely, "because sister Celusa Tamburini notified me that you both have been awake in the hospital for a number of days now."

"Yes, that's right," confirmed Ernesto, "and we are grateful for your time."

"Professor," interrupted Mrs. Serpa confidently, "we've heard so many absurd comments during the short time we've been in our new surroundings. I would like to know if we are free to ask you about anything, anything that seems strange to us."

"Oh, by all means! Ask me anything, although I'm not sure I can answer it all."

Encouraged by Claudio's attentive gaze, Ernesto spoke again:

"I think Evelina has a crucial question on her mind. Maybe this will sound like the foolishness of mental patients – which sometimes we both believe we are – but we have heard on many occasions that everyone here is dead and that we are recovering in an environment that no longer belongs to people of flesh and blood ... At first, we had a good laugh, believing such a notion to be utter silliness; however, we've been hearing it more and more. Even Mrs. Tamburini is certain we have crossed the boundaries of death, just like someone waking up after a night of sleep ... What can you tell us about that, Professor?"

Brother Claudio's face expressed a mixture of surprise and compassion, and he stated with simplicity:

"Are you ready to believe me if I tell you that we are, in fact, living in the Spirit Realm?"

"But Professor..." exclaimed Evelina, very pale.

"I understand," said Claudio, smiling kindly. "You, much more than our brother Ernesto, mentally resist facing the truth because of your praiseworthy but provisional religious convictions, convictions that are deeply rooted in your mind ... Despite all that, however, it is my duty to assure you that we are no longer on the earth, but in an area of the spirit life."

Evelina exclaimed:

"My God, how can that be?"

"Sister Evelina, think about it like this. We arrive on the earth through the maternal womb, go through the period of childhood, and then through an extensive work of re-adaptation; isn't this the same thing?"

"But the earth ... I know about it."

"Not really. We classify earth's landscape and everything it entails according to the concepts of all those who came before us. The same happens here, where we also rely on expert geologists and geographers ... But the truth is that both there and here we know essentially very little about the environment in which we live. In short, we only analyze and re-analyze principles and things that we find already in existence."

"Nevertheless, in the world – as we understand the world – we're certain that we are living on a foundation of solid matter."

"Sister Evelina, who ever said that we didn't also live there in the earthly sphere within a certain level of perception of our eternal spirit? Any student of elementary science is aware of the fact that so-called dense matter is nothing but condensed radiant energy. When all's said and done, we'll discover that matter is *coagulated light*, a divine substance that suggests the omnipresence of God.

"Are you *actually confirming* that we are no longer living on the physical plane?" asked Fantini.

"Whether we call this world 'the other life,' 'the other side,' 'the extra-physical region' or 'the realm of spirits,' the fact is that we are now in a center of physical activity as material as the one inhabited by human beings, our still-incarnate brothers, and we are conditioned to the types of impressions that still dominate nearly all their sensorial resources. The terrestrial world is what human thought makes of it. Here, it is the same thing. Matter is nothing more than energy. Here, as well as there, what is seen is the temporary projection of our mental creations."

"Then, *dying?!* ... What's the purpose? What's the importance in realizing that our lives continue?"

"The unknown factors of outer life and the challenges resulting from them are still the same. However, if individuals would truly aspire to do a self-examination they would find in this new world fascinating surprises in the study and rediscovery of themselves. Each one of us is a world of intelligence searching for ... and perfecting ourselves."

Ernesto kept up his questioning:

"Are all the dead everywhere on the earth in situations identical to ours?"

"That would be impossible. Let's take a quick look at incarnate humankind, and we will understand something on this subject. On the earth, where we have come from, there are millions of people who are either sane or mentally unbalanced, healthy or ill, educated or unlearned, relatively evolved or excessively animalized, trusting or disbelieving, advanced in their evolution or just beginners. It would be impracticable to classify them after death according to an exclusive criterion. Each spirit will find itself in its own group and each group in its own community or plane of affinity. It isn't easy to standardize the circumstances of discarnate spirits. It's enough to remember that every day about 150,000[8] individuals leave the physical environment at an average of 100 per minute, leaving behind affections, achievements, commitments, problems ... Well, they are all God's children and they all receive equal attention and assistance from God with respect to the love with which we are enveloped in his creation, although such attention and assistance differ in the many ways in which they are expressed. It is reasonable to conceive that, for whatever they might have been, no matter how much human beings are adorned with the honors paid to them by their loved ones when they leave the world, they arrive here as they really are ... Just because they have disincarnated, the madman does not acquire reason overnight, nor does the unlearned person obtain knowledge by osmosis. After death we are what we have made of ourselves in our inner reality, and we end up in a place that is compatible with our potential for recuperation or with the opportunities for service displayed by us."

"We're talking about an enormous amount of work!" exclaimed Fantini in amazement.

"Yes, in the world of men and women, people do not suddenly change simply because they have crossed the ocean from one continent to another ... The same applies to the realm of spirits."

"Some time ago," Ernesto pointed out, "I read some messages of trustworthy discarnate spirits telling about their suffering and conflicts in the lower zones; individuals who, by the way, seemed to possess vast intellectual capabilities."

"That's nothing to marvel at. Due to the demands of our needs, we ourselves are living in one such region that is located close to incarnate individuals."

---

[8] Data from 1968. – Tr.

"But I'm referring to the horrific or unhappy regions that I heard so many lectures about, and where our brothers and sisters suffer terribly."

"Fantini," explained the instructor, "we must realize that those places are not unhappy; rather, the brothers and sisters who populate them are. Do the gardens and orchards around an insane asylum cease to be gardens and orchards merely because their flowers and fruit are enjoyed by un-well persons?"

"I'm not following."

"Well, my friend, the sometimes enormous areas of space occupied by legions of suffering or disturbed souls are circumscribed and guarded, no matter how large they are, just like places on the earth used by large institutions for the recovery of mental patients. You are aware of the fact that there are mentally ill patients who spend most of their lives in asylums. The same happens here. There is a vast territory around our colony that is used as an asylum for thousands of maladjusted brothers and sisters that are looked after and watched over by many beneficent organizations that work in the area of fraternal assistance."

Evelina couldn't believe what she was hearing. She interrupted, dissatisfied:

"But ... if we are on a plane in the spirit world, how do you explain all these solid buildings that resemble earth's architecture?"

"That's nothing extraordinary if we remember that buildings in the world of humans originate in the thought that designs them and the matter that conforms to the blueprints. Here, the process is the same, the only difference lying in the nature of matter, which is much more malleable to the influence of the dominant idea. Let's recall the current progress of the plastics industry down on the physical plane and we will most surely understand the immense possibilities for elegant and complex buildings here. Of course, here too we are still subject to techniques, vocations, personal talent and stylistic creations in the circle of individual spiritual achievements. The architect who plans a house and the builder who follows his directions cannot immediately take the place of the manager of a textile factory and the worker who follows his or her orders. Also, here a writer does not all of a sudden and without proper training compose the works of a musician. We are evolving creatures who have not yet reached the state of multi-faceted geniuses, although such geniuses also do in fact exist here."

Mrs. Serpa couldn't hide her disbelief.

"All this seems so implausible," she said.

"Nothing is more implausible to us than the truth," objected Brother Claudio. "Nonetheless, reality does not stop being reality just because for a long time we have opted for illusion instead."

The professor continued to speak for several minutes regarding the life and conditions of their present habitat, but finally Evelina felt lightheaded, tired and temporarily unable to follow any more explanations. However, as a woman of deep faith she took advantage of a pause in the conversation to ask:

"Brother Claudio, I cannot doubt what you're saying, although it's very difficult for me to believe we are discarnate, according to what you have said. Please rest assured that I do not wish to waste your guidance in any way, but I would like to get in touch with a priest, a Catholic priest, for instance ... I would be happy if I could continue to go to confession, to exchange ideas freely with a cleric of the faith that shaped my character, without any hindrance to my social life."

The kind instructor smiled sympathetically and explained:

"The Church here is completely different, although in the surrounding areas in which thousands upon thousands of rebellious and troubled minds have congregated, we can find representatives of all earth's religions who are still stuck in dogmas, narrow-minded concepts and many kinds of prejudices and tyranny deriving from fanaticism. Here, the priests would not hear your confession in a religious manner. They would send you to one of our institutes of supportive psychiatry, where you can and should have your chart in order to receive the assistance you need ..."

"For our treatment?" interrupted Fantini.

"Treatment and assistance. An enrollment card from the support and analysis services at one of the places of spiritual supervision I just mentioned is a valuable document, so that during our initial phase of adapting to this new realm – an intermediate place between lower and higher planes – we can receive the appropriate assistance. It is essential that we spare ourselves unnecessary anguish as much as possible."

"Oh!" exclaimed Ernesto enthusiastically, "I would be interested in that type of confession ... if we actually are dead."

"Your *if*," said the mentor with good cheer, "implies that you and Evelina think I am a fiction storyteller ... You're both discarnate all right, yet with roots still buried in earthly soil; but that is natural. You just need time."

Surrounded by the pure vibrations of trust and sympathy, Mrs. Serpa and Fantini asked Claudio's help to contact one of the local psychiatric institutions. It was agreed that they would tend to this as soon as the hospital gave them permission.

10
Evelina Serpa

Duly authorized, Evelina and Ernesto reached the Institute of Spiritual Watch Care after a short walk along the charming streets of the city.

They were kindly greeted by Instructor Ribas, who worked in the assistance department of the psychiatric clinic. They felt as comfortable as if they were visiting a modern office down on earth. Everything denoted simplicity, comfort and security. There were attendants; files; special devices to register thoughts.

After the introductions, the medical instructor broached the subject:

"We have been informed that the two of you will be enrolled in our department.

We'll start with our sister Evelina."

Without further ado, he gestured to an employee whom he called Brother Telmo. Assigning Ernesto to him, he stated:

"You two stay here while I hear what sister Evelina has to say."

To a highly concerned Fantini, he stated:

"There's nothing to be concerned about. All conversation here at our Institute is geared toward encouragement and health. No negative thoughts. As soon as I finish the initial session with our friend here, you and I will have our own time together."

The congenial atmosphere was so spontaneous and natural that the two newcomers couldn't figure out what their situation really was.

Were they in the spirit world or on the earth – the earth that was so familiar to them – in some unknown place where they were being told about the *liberated spirit* for therapeutic purposes? They almost believed that perhaps they really had been insane but were now beginning to recover.

Harboring such doubts, Evelina obediently followed the doctor. They went into a room that was tastefully and modestly furnished, and as she sat in the armchair he had indicated to her, Ribas explained kindly:

"There's no cause for alarm. Our Institute is dedicated to the safety and watch care of its wards. The initial assistance comes first, and then the readjustment if necessary. So, this will be strictly casual. Nothing formal. We'll simply have a chat and everything you say will be recorded for later study. In fact, my job here is merely to orient our patients, since they have access to a large network of support made up of individuals who examine their words and reactions in order to know how and to what extent they will provide the assistance they need."

As Evelina watched in wonder, the instructor made a gesture and a large mirror appeared near her chair. It looked like it was plugged into the electrical system by means of a special device.

"Our talk will be videoed. It's a simple way to guarantee that your contacts with our institute will be safely monitored regarding the assistance you will need during your first period of spirit life. Don't be concerned, but do bear in mind that all your questions and answers are extremely important for us to be able to help you. The Institute will use your questions to determine the extent of your current understanding, and your answers will show it the extent of your needs. So let's get started."

Before those kind yet firm eyes, Evelina felt like a grade school girl before an experienced examiner, and concluding that she could not refuse the test, she asked with respectful courage:

"Instructor Ribas, you said my *first period of spirit life*. So, it's true that we are discarnate spirits, persons no longer living on the earth?"

"That's right, even though you haven't yet grasped the fact."

"Why am I having such a hard time adapting?"

"Lack of preparation while incarnate. Generally speaking, your state of astonishment is common to most human beings and is due to the absence of a true integration with the religious beliefs they hold dear."

"If we really are *dead*, do you think that as a Catholic I should or would display a higher level of understanding of spiritual truth than I have been?"

"Yes, I do."

"How so?"

"If during your existence in the physical body you had thought deeply about the teachings of Jesus, the Divine Master who arose from the tomb in a demonstration of the life eternal; if you had meditated on the essence of the religious rituals of your faith, which are all dedicated to God; and after God, dedicated to the holy dead such as Our Lord Jesus Christ, his August Mother and the noble spirits whom we venerate as saints of the Christian life, you certainly wouldn't be experiencing the astonishment that up till now has been desensitizing your energy centers, despite the loftiness and sublimity of your aspirations."

Evelina was suddenly transported by the magic wings of imagination back to her old church ... She remembered the prayers, the songs and the liturgical rites that were part of her life as if only there, in that room of spiritual analysis, could she grasp their real meaning. Why hadn't she been led earlier to see that they were invocations to the spirit world? Why hadn't she realized until just now their role as channels of communication with the Divine Powers?

In thought she yearned to be back in Sao Paulo, to walk to the place of her religious devotion and acknowledge in her own faith the highest point of life, through which she could surrender to the care of the All-Merciful with her joys and pains, her innermost afflictions and anxieties ... Whether in sculptures or paintings, in sermons and conversations, she remembered Jesus as being a Divine Spirit knocking at her door in vain, trying to teach her to live and understand.

As she reflected on the Master of infinite patience, into whose magnanimity she always commended herself in all difficulties and tribulations without bothering to understand his teachings or to follow his example, she burst into tears – as if her pious and compassionate Christian faith had become a judge in the recesses of her soul, reproaching her behavior.

"Oh, my God!" she exclaimed in tears. "Why did I have to *die* to finally get it? Why, Lord? Why?!"

She was in this place for a moral accounting; she was here to talk about herself and to analyze what she had done. What had she carried in her life's baggage except the emptiness of an existence that now seemed useless? She had the feeling that the mental barriers that had kept her from the eternal realities had suddenly broken down, that she could feel the lightness of thought that had overcome her, and that this Jesus whom she had worshiped outwardly had now entered the recesses of her heart and was asking her with infinite tenderness, "Evelina, what have you done with me?"

Somewhat out of control, Mrs. Serpa wept convulsively in front of the Instructor, who looked at her like a father.

Her caring new friend waited for her to stop crying, and when she had finally composed herself he said kindly:

"This temporary angst is good for you. Mental pain measures our notion of responsibility. Your suffering as a spirit upon remembering Jesus proves your trust in him."

In a more tender tone, the Instructor set the analysis on a new course and informed the young woman that her identification log was ready, that before her arrival the health institution through which she had entered the city had been consulted regarding her origin and filiation on the earth.

Even so, he added:

"However, what you tell us here will be invaluable because we can use it to become more amply informed as to how best to assist you."

"Can you tell me what kind of assistance it will be?"

"We'll be able to decide on the type of support to give you based on what you yourself tell us."

"But Instructor Ribas, aren't I known in the spirit world already? Don't we all have guardian angels while on the earth?"

"Certainly. And all of them who know us have a particular version of our experiences for their own use. In our studies, however, your own personal version is the most important because your autobiographical information will pour forth from your own conscience. We need to promote a self-encounter at the level of the realities of the soul in order to reach the precise balance of our immediate needs. Of course, your name will appear elsewhere and will be cited by many fellow spirits, displayed in the impressions you may have caused them. But here in our institute we will collect your individual, non-transferable projection."

Then, amid the expectations of his surprised client, the Instructor asked her to tell him about a few passages of her life's story, starting with her earliest memories. He asked her to avoid too much detail, trying instead to summarize information and memories as much as possible.

Mrs. Serpa began meekly:

"My foggy memories start at the time I lost my father. I was very young when I heard my mother crying as she held me close and told me I was fatherless ... But a short time later she gave me a good and kind stepfather. Upon her second marriage, she and my new father decided to leave the area, obviously because they wanted to flee unwelcome memories. Despite the tenderness of the man who had become the head of our household, I instinctively missed my real father. However, the information I received about him was always scanty. I couldn't get a thing from my mother regarding his death except that he had died suddenly on an outing ... When I was a bit older, I realized that she was hesitant to talk about the past in order to avoid possible conflicts with her new husband, who, I must say, loves her dearly to this day ... When I was twelve, I was sent to a Catholic boarding school, from which I graduated as a teacher. I never taught, however, because as soon as I graduated, I was courted by two young men at the same time: Tulio Mancini and Caio Serpa. I must confess that, since I was still quite young and very irresponsible, I let my heart waver between the two and I promised fidelity to both of them. When I finally announced that my final choice was Caio, who later became my husband, Tulio tried to commit suicide. After he pulled through, I thought of the sacrifice he had made for my sake, and I leaned back toward him ... Just when I was about to break up with my fiancée Caio, Tulio shot himself in the heart ... After that terrible event, I got married ... Caio and I were happy for a few months until we saw our wish to have a child dampened ... I lost the baby soon after getting pregnant. Right after that my health began to deteriorate. Maybe because of the illness that attacked me without respite, Caio went looking for new companionship and found a single girl, whom he started seeing in the big city ... The shameful situation devastated me. The constant humiliation to which I was exposed at home made my life bitter ... After that, I guess there's nothing else to confess except mental suffering and a lack of the will to live due to the illness I had been treated for until I got here."

Moved, the Instructor looked at her and asked:

"Have you forgiven your unfaithful husband and taken pity on your rival?"

Mrs. Serpa thought for a few moments and answered bitterly:

"No, I haven't. I'm making a confession with Jesus as my witness and I cannot lie. I could never forgive my husband for his disloyalty or tolerate the presence of the *other* on our path."

Far from being shocked, the Instructor responded kindly:

"I understand your human sentiments and we can finish today's session. You have some difficult problems to deal with and our Institute will evaluate to what extent it can give you the help you need. We'll keep in touch and will continue to talk in future sessions."

Evelina left the room and was replaced by Fantini, whose session was about to begin.

11
Ernesto Fantini

It was Ernesto's turn. He sat down in the armchair somewhat disconcerted. The Instructor went through the explanations he had given Evelina, told Ernesto to ask any questions he wished, and turned on the mirror-recorder.

Fantini felt a little more at ease and began the session:

"May I speak as if I really am dead, as I have been told?"

Instructor Ribas smiled at hearing that question, so typical of an intelligent materialist, and replied without being curt:

"Ask anything you'd like, but you can be certain that the theory of *as if* is now far behind us. We are in fact discarnate, and we are now in ..."

"Instructor, if I left my body behind on the earth without remembering having done so, then upon returning to the spirit's natural habitat, shouldn't I be able to remember the time I lived as a free spirit before having assumed that body? Why hasn't that happened?"

"Besides being a stage of learning, healing, redemption or a specific task, life in the physical body is also a long immersion in magnetic conditioning, through which we act in the world, leading us to do what we need to do. In terms of our own conscience, free will remains alive and untouched, since the incarnate individual is at liberty to choose his or her own direction in every circumstance. However, during incarnation, the soul's remaining potentialities continue to be guided towards this or that endeavor according to the commitments it had assumed or had been forced to assume before incarnating.

"This fact causes our past memories to become veiled, which is only a temporary phenomenon that is longer or shorter depending on one's degree of evolution."

"So, while in the physical realm we were under the influence of an extended hypnosis?"

"To a certain degree, yes. The passage through the maternal womb, the new name chosen by the family, the seven years of semi-consciousness in the parental household's atmosphere, the recapitulation of childhood, the return to adolescence and the problems of adulthood, with its consequent responsibilities and commitments, build in us – the eternal individuality – a new personality, which we incorporate into our trove of experiences. It only makes sense that during the time immediately after discarnation, our long-term memory is still hermetically sealed in the depths of our being. This situation is only temporary, of course. Bit by bit, our memories come back to us."

"So, you're telling me that here in this city I am still Ernesto Fantini, the human personality with the name that was given to me in the existence I left behind, and that the examination of my previous memories is being deferred until later?"

"Exactly. Each one of us lives here in centers of work and renewal in a realm close to the physical one, using the same name by which we were known there. Until we promote ourselves to higher spheres through our own merit, we must remain between Higher Spirituality and the Physical Stage, working on our personal development from our internment in the cradle to our deliverance to the spirit life, and then regressing from the freedom of the spirit life to a new internment in the cradle. Understand?"

"So, we are examined here by what we were and what we did during our latest past life?"

"That's right."

"As far as our personal file is concerned we remain just as we always have been until..."

"Until the circumstances indicate that it is time for a new immersion in the physical body as the only way to proceed with our personal evolution in the struggles of the life eternal."

"Are we exactly as we always were in every way, even our morphological characteristics?"

"Not really. Any morphological traits can be modified under the influence of mental commands. This happens all the time in the human world itself. It isn't hard for science to modify the implements of an individual's reproductive apparatus in accordance with the psychological impulses that that individual displays, thereby harmonizing the body-soul duality. Moreover, we mustn't forget the multiform uses of plastic surgery, which can work wonders on people's physical envelope if they deserve the improvements that generous and optimistic earthly science offers them."

Fantini was pleasantly surprised by the mental dexterity with which the Instructor placed the precise explanations in his enlightenment-thirsty mind.

"My dear friend," he stated, "although I've already discussed this topic with Brother Claudio, I would like to hear what you have to say about it ... He said that some of the dead – even the knowledgeable ones – spend years and years tormented in the lower regions before regaining their lucidity and peace of mind; why didn't I have to go through that if I really am discarnate and a man aware of his wrongs?"

"The state of tribulation you are referring to pertains to the spirit and not the place. Many of us discarnates experience times of difficulty in certain places that reflect our personal inner turmoil. This anomaly can last for a long time, depending on our inclinations and the effort we make to accept ourselves – imperfect as we still are – even though we are aware of our need to evolve as established by the laws of life. For the time being, we are indebted consciences or we are examples of deficient evolution before the Greater Life. We bear the duty of purging our flaws through honest, constant labor. As long as we are imbalanced after discarnation – an imbalance that is always worsened by our non-conformity, rebelliousness, pride or despair, which in turn threatens the safety of others – it makes sense for us to remain interned or isolated in certain regions along with those who display disturbances or conflicts similar to our own. We are like mental patients who cannot live at home so that they can receive the treatment they need."

"So, notions about *being punished by God...*"

"It is understandable why we have to believe them until we learn that Divine Providence governs us through wise and impartial laws. We all punish ourselves according to the articles of the Heavenly Statutes that we have broken. Eternal Justice operates in the inner forum of each individual and determines that responsibility be measured according to one's level of knowledge."

"Instructor Ribas, in light of all this, how are we to regard the hell invented by the religions down on earth?"

"We need to address the subject with the respect it demands, because, for millions of souls, their mental torment alongside others in the same situation can be rightly compared to the suffering described by the theological hell imagined by human belief systems. But seriously speaking, and bearing in mind the reality that God never forsakes us, hell should be seen as a kind of asylum where we suffer the consequences of our wrongs, which, in fact, we committed against ourselves. It is easy to understand that the region in which we linger in this grievous situation is a representation of the unhappy mental pictures that we create and project around us."

"I would dare to probe so many issues because I believe wholeheartedly that there is no way that I deserve the generosity being shown to me ... I have enjoyed a peacefulness here that I would not expect, since I bear within me a painful problem of conscience."

"One of the functions of our Institution is precisely that of supporting discarnate brothers and sisters who arrive here with their moral integrity undamaged, but bearing guilt complexes that can drive them to making greater changes. Our help is rendered more effective the stronger the individual's faith regarding his or her potential for overcoming the weaknesses that are peculiar to us. Your psychological structure has immunized you against the delirium of many good and worthy people, who must often undergo cleansing afflictions in the large asylums we mentioned earlier in order to heal the imbalances they so often fell into for having given the wrong direction to the love with which they were nourished."

Ribas paused, smiled and stated:

"Even so, despite your splendid level of resistance, you are not shielded from the consequences of what you did and you must face them as soon as possible."

"Please, explain what you mean."

"We mean to say that you must have enough peace of mind to go to those you left behind in the world so that you can understand both yourself and them ... In the physical realm we often hear it said that one must have courage to see and hear the dead! The situation here is no different in relation to the so-called living. Generally speaking, all of us are taken immediately after discarnation to preparatory courses in understanding in order to acquire the courage we need to see and hear the living again without harming either them or us."

"Ernesto's eyes nearly popped out of their sockets at hearing these warnings. Heavy tears ran down his face, while, as if due to the pressure of invisible springs forcing him to blurt out the thoughts of guilt hidden in the recesses of his soul, he fell on his knees before his benefactor like a frightened child and blurted:

"Instructor, as far as I know, I'm guilty of only one wrong, but it is enough to have created many hells in my mind. I killed a friend more than twenty years ago, and I've never had a moment's peace since ... I knew he held shameful intentions for my wife as he followed her comings and goings ... I saw him watching my house while I was away ... On occasion, I heard him speaking inappropriately to the woman who shared my name ... One day I thought I saw in my wife's eyes a certain inclination toward this enemy of my peace of mind, and before I could confirm my suspicions, I took advantage of what seemed the right moment and shot him while three of us were hunting quail ... I shot to kill. With my plan satisfied, I hid in the brush until the third hunter found the body and sounded the alarm ... The victim landed on the ground in such a way that it looked to everybody like it had been an accident ... Horrified at my crime, I eagerly went along with this wrong interpretation ... But I never recovered my peace of mind. Like myself, the man I killed was married, and I never got up the courage to look for his family, who was anxious to forget the tragedy and left the area soon afterward ... However, I couldn't forget ... It seemed like the death I had caused brought my fearsome enemy right into my own home ... After that horrific event I began to feel his presence as a relentless shadow that mocked and insulted me without the others ever noticing it ... I felt shackled to him there as if the wretch was growing more alive and stronger every day ... Before the surgery that resulted in my coming here, there were very few nights when I didn't struggle with him in my dreams ... I would wake up as if we had fought a deadly duel, only to see him with the eyes of my imagination, sharing my daily life! ... Ah! Instructor Ribas! Instructor Ribas! ... In the name of God, tell me if there is a cure for me! ... After death I expected a place of punishment where the powers of hell would charge me for the crime I had hidden from earth's justice; but here, I'm enjoying a kind of care that only deepens my inner torment! ... Ah! ... My friend, my friend, what will become of me? I can't stand myself."

Having said this, Fantini embraced his counselor, sobbing like a helpless boy begging for safety.

The Instructor gathered him in a fatherly embrace and consoled him:

"Compose yourself, my son! ... We are eternal spirits and God our Father will never leave us helpless."

Ribas' eyes held tears that didn't fall. It seemed that he, the competent guide, had had his own experience with such suffering of conscience, because, rather than reprimanding Ernesto, he patted his tired head, which he had rested on his knees, and concluded simply:

"God's Justice does not come without the support of mercy. Let's be trustful!"

And without further delay, Ribas got up, visibly moved, turned off the mirror and ended the session.

12
Judgment and Love

After a few weeks Ernesto and Evelina felt less awkward in their environment.

Although they still cherished their loved ones, they felt more and more attached to each other. Noticeably better, they had not left the hospital yet, but were now living in convalescent wards, each in their own place; the wards housed men and women in huge clusters of apartment homes for individual use. They had permission to move about as they pleased in the city, but were told that they could visit the outskirts inhabited by thousands of miserable spirits only if they had adequate assistance.

Actually, both of them had begun to feel the need for disciplined and regular work, but if they asked for work or anything else having to do with their former homes on the earth, which they had not yet been able to visit, the answer they received from the authorities was always the same: they should wait a bit longer; they needed to be properly prepared. Consequently, they frequented libraries, gardens and institutions, and they took part in various leisure activities. Life there seemed like a long phase of mental repose at a peaceful holiday resort. The day finally came, however, for Evelina to realize one of her biggest dreams in that place of blessing. With the consent of their benefactors, Fantini had promised to take her to a religious temple in order to attend the evening service, which, as announced beforehand, would entail a sermon entitled "Judgment and Love." Both Ernesto and Evelina were burning with curiosity because they were eager to see for themselves how religious matters played out in that world so extremely beautiful and new to them.

At nightfall they set out.

On the way, Mrs. Serpa recalled how she used to visit the sanctuary of her faith, and she harbored the sweetest memories in her soul.

Moved, she thought to herself: How had she lost contact with her dearest loved ones and why was she walking arm in arm with a man she had met only once while on earth?

Around them the soft breeze carried the fragrance of gardens and squares in bloom.

The moon above the horizon was the same spectacle of majesty and beauty she had been accustomed to in the world.

From time to time she exchanged one or two sentences with Fantini, noticing that other like-minded groups were heading in the same direction.

After a few minutes of pleasant walking, they reached the temple. It was transcendent in its simplicity, looking like an enormous dovecote built from strips of translucent snow, protected here and there by dense groves of trees.

Inside, everything suggested spontaneity and harmony.

The long rows of pews allowed a view of the pulpit, which looked like an enormous lily sculpted in snow-white marble.

On the bright white wall in front of the congregation and under the inscriptions: "Temple of the New Revelation" and "Place Consecrated to the Worship of Our Lord Jesus Christ," there was, instead of symbols or statues, just one exquisite painting showing the probable likeness of the Divine Master, whose eyes seemed to speak of life and omnipresence.

As she sat next to Fantini, Mrs. Serpa observed the faces around them, some serene and others anxious, but all in deep silence. She immersed her heart in silent prayer.

Suddenly, as if he had suddenly materialized at the pulpit or had arrived there through a door hidden from the congregation, a man appeared. He was dressed in a snow-white cloak and greeted the assembly reverently.

He gazed toward heaven, and in a moving prayer he beseeched Jesus' blessings on the expectant congregation.

Then, he approached a large copy of the New Testament that lay open on an elegant lectern, and read Matthew 7:1-4:

Do not judge, so that you may not be judged, for in the same way that you judge others, you will be judged; and with the measure by which you measure, you will be measured.

Why do you see the speck in your brother's eye but do not notice the plank in your own? Or how can you say to your brother, 'Let me take the speck out of your eye,' when there is a plank in yours?

When he had finished the reading, the minister remained in profound concentration as if looking for inspiration in the depths of his soul.

Ernesto and Evelina were astonished to see that his thought was starting to materialize in the shape of a broad, flame-like halo of light rising from the top of his head and going higher and higher.

A few seconds later, flashes of light poured down from above, reminiscent of the tongues of fire on the Day of

Pentecost. The kind minister began his sermon, of which we will reproduce only a few passages that define its content of wisdom and beauty:

"Brothers and sisters, until yesterday all of us were an integral part of the human community – our blessed family left behind – and we thought that we could judge one another. Ensconced in the religious ideas that we believed we could enslave to serve our passions, we thought that anyone who did not subscribe to our own principles was an adversary and wrongdoer.

"We interpreted the teachings of Our Lord Jesus Christ as we saw fit, demanding the Lord of Life to be our lowly servant on the gloomy and tormenting road we strove to walk. However, rid of the body of dense matter that used to harbor our illusions, we have learned that we are all indebted consciences before the Law. And fortunately for us, we now understand that only the Lord has the resources to judge us rightly, because truthfully, we can evaluate only ourselves.

"Whatever we were at the core of our sentiments while in the earthly body, we continue to be here.

"In this refuge of light which the Lord grants us as a temporary home, we realize without any outward constraints that all the devices we used for maintaining the appearances that disguised us in the world for the role we were supposed to perform on the human stage have been taken from us so that here in the sphere of spiritual reality we can be the persons we were meant to be, with everything we gathered inside of us, whether good or bad, during our stay in the physical school!

"Many of you still carry habits and illusions from the corporeal experience; you will gradually lose them, for they have no meaning in this realm.

"Your castles or hovels, your conventional titles or disparaging labels, your privileges or imprisonments, your family honors or public disrespect, your gains or superficial losses, in short, all of the mental conditioning that centered you on the idea of supposed rights or imaginary complaints as you forsook the natural duty of spiritual growth toward the life eternal disappeared on the day when others saw your name written on a death certificate when you discarnated, and they took possession of your assets and judged your actions. Later, most of them banished you from their thought with the erroneous belief that they could expel you from their memory forever!

"How many of you have come here to listen to the voices of truth to which you so many times shut your earthly ears?

"Divine Providence does not ask us what we were, for it knows every one of us at any given time ... It merely asks how we used the treasure of time that was granted to all of us equally.

"You learned individuals, how did you use your gifts of advanced knowledge? You less-educated, what did you do with your treasure of time? You wealthy, in what kind of work did you dignify your money? Brothers and sisters deprived of wealth but so often bearers of greater blessings, what did you do with the opportunities you were given to show patience, service, understanding and humility in the area of obedience? You young people, what did you do with your strength? Fellow spirits whose hair grew white on the daily trek, in what good deeds did you apply the light of your understanding?

"Do not deceive yourselves!

"Just as was the case for we who have inhabited the spirit realm for many decades, you have brought here only what you made of yourselves ... You have learned what you studied, you show what you did, you possess what you gave away!

"In short, after having crossed the Great Boundary, we are simply what we are!

"Thus, you will realize day by day in this place of blessed reality that all the disguises that used to hide our true individuality in the world are erased naturally, exposing our inner realm.

"Without the constraints of the body, each spirit reveals who it really is.

"In the ancestral home of the soul, we mechanically imprint our attitudes and words with the sentiments and thoughts that are particular to us; we can no longer fake it.

"Displaying everything we are and everything we have in the recesses of our being, the time for judgment has arrived, because the Divine Mercy of the Lord still offers to us, as in other colonies in the spirit world, this city-home as the antechamber for study and service. It gives us the invaluable potential to prepare our ascension to the Greater Life, in whose provinces we will apply ourselves in the acquisition of as-yet indescribable aptitudes as we continue the blessed struggle for our spiritual growth.

"However, all those who scorn the sublime opportunities of time on the plane of renovation where we are now harbored will surely leave for neighboring regions, where the agents of perturbation and darkness gather – willingly sick spirits, mistreating one another in pitiful reciprocity – until, exhausted from rebelliousness, they plead for the mercy of the Eternal Laws that they might receive the precious gift of reincarnation of regenerative suffering in order to return to this place, God only knows when!

"We are not saying that rebirth in the physical realm is always a crucible for redeeming the wrongs we have committed, because, after the long and honest effort of self-correction among us here in this colony of work and reform, thousands of fellow spirits return to the physical body to be honored with tasks of selflessness and anonymous heroism alongside another person or kindred group. This way, through laudable anonymity, they acquire concessions and victories worthy of praise, which, in spite of nearly always being ignored by humankind, are transformed here into passports of freedom and purification for the Higher Realms!"

During a spontaneous pause by the speaker, who was surrounded by brilliant light, Evelina and Ernesto looked at each other, and then, glancing quickly at the congregation, they saw that dozens of faces were bathed in tears.

"Brothers and sisters," continued the preacher, "do not feel as if you are facing a court of justice, when, in fact, we are in a house of faith! ... As a loving mother of our impulses of growth and sublimation, faith tells us in this industrious and peaceful place that, in spite of being discarnate, we must remember that our opportunities for work, progress, rectification and learning have not yet come to an end.

"Let us accept who we are, let us acknowledge the amount of our debts, and let us put our faithful hands to the plow of service to our neighbor, without looking back ... This city that unites us is full of beneficent institutions with doors wide open to all volunteers who wish to collaborate in helping those who come to us each and every day in anguish or need ... Down on the earth, where our brothers and sisters fight the hard battle of evolution, our still-incarnate loved ones require from us the most arduous demonstrations of human tenderness by means of the spiritual assistance we may give them through understanding and love so that they may continue to live the earthly experience they need with serenity and happiness without us ... An entire apostolate of constructive renunciation, selflessness, care and understanding has opened up before most of you in your homes on earth, to which nearly all of you are still attached in thought and heart!

"Moreover, we are surrounded on all sides by crowds of demented fellow spirits begging us for love and patience so that they may recover! ... While we were in the physical realm, we sent out pleas for tables dedicated to the hungry and warm clothing for the naked ... Here, we are challenged to build and sustain our devotion and tolerance so that harmony and understanding may be established in the suffering and disturbed souls of our brothers and sisters lost in the darkness of spirit.

"Charity, my brothers and sisters! Love for our neighbor!

"Many times, the work of a few days can grant us a priceless loan of energies and means for undertaking the recuperation and ascension that demand many years of effort.

"Let us pray, asking the Lord to inspire us so that we may courageously choose the road of purification either by means of new and blessed reincarnations in the physical world or the upward pathway to the Greater Life!"

The minister became silent in mute prayer.

From the ceiling, bands of sapphire blue light beamed down like tiny petals, which dissolved upon touching all the participants' heads, or disappeared delicately when they reached the floor.

The minister was concentrating deeply when on his chest blazed a translucent silver star, from whose center gently radiated a rainfall of lily white rays flooding the room.

Fantini was moved, but Evelina – as was the case with many of the spirits gathered there – could not hold back the tears that came in a growing wave from her heart to her eyes.

Mrs. Serpa would not be able to explain the reason for the emotion that had assailed the recesses of her soul. Extremely touched as she was, she didn't know if she owed those blessed tears to her longing for heaven or for the earth ... She didn't hear the minister's final words as he ended the evening service. She only knew that now she sought complete support on the arm of her friend, with whom she left the premises, sobbing...

13
New Tasks

Deeply touched by what they had heard in the temple, Evelina and Ernesto asked to be admitted to Brother Claudio's traveling assistance group, which made weekly visits to the region of disturbed and suffering spirits.

Their friend from the Institute of Spirit Sciences kindly and benevolently granted their request, and a few days later, our two friends were actively taking part in a work group of eight persons – five men and three women. One of them was Sister Celusa Tamburini.

On its fraternal mission the team descended toward a large valley with the specific objective that day of participating in the Gospel at Home[9] meeting at Ambrosio and Priscila's. The couple worked as guardians along with the many others placed along the border that marked out the initial points of the region assaulted by the mental projections of disturbed brothers and sisters.

---

[9] Weekly home gatherings for the reading and study of the Gospel and for prayer. – Tr.

After they had crossed a broad area of the landscape, Ernesto and Evelina couldn't hide their astonishment. A thick fog of several shades of gray formed a dividing line along the whole border. For the first time, they saw in the sky the flying machines that were on their way from the city to the land of darkness. They looked like huge, silent butterflies reflecting the sunlight with wings that seemed to be made of bits of the rainbow.

Fantini immediately asked about them and Claudio explained kindly:

"Those are flying devices that work teams use for traveling on tasks of identification and assistance."

"Is the region that big?"

"Imagine an enormous planetary desert surrounded by orderly, prosperous cities and you will get a precise idea of what goes on there."

"And those who travel by air: since they are discarnate, wouldn't it be easier for them to do without these vehicles and just use volitation[10]?"

The leader smiled and considered:

"Everything in life is governed by laws. A bird has wings and flees the burning field because it cannot tolerate the clouds of smoke. A fireman wears protective clothing in order to get into a burning house."

And he added:

"We are headed for a dangerous expanse of space inhabited by thousands of rebellious spirits who have constructed their desolate environment with their own deranged thoughts. There, in that different world, we see the strangest constructions, all of them caricatures of the homes their owners misused during their physical experience. It is a veritable forest of condensed fluids, out-

---

[10] A spirit's ability to move through the air without touching the ground. – Tr.

picturing the ideas, habits, ambitions, caprices, remorse and regret of its dwellers. That segment of the lower regions is in a completely anarchical state. Individualism distorts the idea of freedom without the beneficial constraints of discipline, which makes us truly free through willing submission to the provisions of God's Laws."

"And why does God allow the formation of such huge pockets of disturbance and disorder?" asked Ernesto in a dash of human logic.

"Ah, my friend!" answered Brother Claudio, "Whenever we ask our Superiors why Divine Providence doesn't interfere with the mind corrupted by evil, the invariable answer is that the Creator demands that individuals be left free to choose the kind of evolutionary path that seems best to them, be it an avenue of stars or a pathway of mire. God wants all his children to have their own individuality, to believe in him as they can, to preserve the tendencies and preferences that are most in keeping with their way of being, to work however and as much as they please, and to live wherever they want. He only demands – and strictly – that justice be done and respected. 'To each according to his deeds.' Through the Laws of Life we will all receive according to what we have done, how much we have done, and how we have done it. In accordance with the Divine Precepts, we can live and associate with others in keeping with the patterns of choice and affection we have chosen. However, on any plane of consciousness, from the lowest to the most sublime, harm to one's neighbor, affronts against others, criminality and ingratitude reap painful and unavoidable readjustments according to the principles of cause and effect, imposing dire punishment on offenders. We are free to develop, cultivate and perfect our tendencies, but we must abide by the Statutes of the Eternal Good, whose articles and clauses state that the guarantees of our own well-being are based and maintained on goodness for all and selfless assistance to others."

Reaching the dark border of the strange hamlet, ragged and alienated individuals began to appear here and there.

One could not say that they were similar to the poverty-stricken street beggars down on the earth. Some of the inhabitants of those vast outskirts seemed like pride or indifference had turned them into spiritually distant creatures. Others appeared full of irony and scorn because of the jeering mimicry with which they pointed at or addressed the travelers. Almost all wore strange clothing, each depicting the status and decorations which they believed were theirs.

To one of Fantini's questions – he and Evelina were the only newcomers on the assistance team – Claudio replied:

"Generally speaking, the thousands of brothers and sisters who live in this region do not accept themselves as they are. They have grown so accustomed to the often- necessary likenesses of the physical experience that they feel offended by the truth. They lived years and years in the physical realm enjoying this or that benefit by means of the superficial values they proudly displayed, and they don't accept the suppression of the illusion and imaginary privileges that used to nourish them ... Like Narcissus, they are fixated on their own image in the past ... After discarnation many of them went directly from their physical life to that gloomy place, whereas others came to live in cities of recovery and education similar to ours. However, as they gradually revealed themselves as they really are, without any of the disguises they utilized on the earth to hide their true 'self', they rebelled against the light of the spirit world because it exposes one's true nature to everyone else, and they fled our communities, taking refuge in this valley of darkness that they themselves have created. There, in the penumbra created by their own mental energies for the purpose of hiding themselves, they give way in varying degrees to the manifestations of the paranoia they cultivate, and in many cases they give in to deplorable passions, which, in vain, they try to satiate until they almost go crazy."

"Brother Claudio," asked Evelina, "have you ever gone much beyond the border of one of these places?"

"Using different vehicles, I have gone on several missions of fraternity and assistance very far from where we are at the moment."

"And what did you see?"

"Cities, towns, villages and hamlets, where spirits with vigorous and educated but deeply perverted minds dominate huge groups of spirits who are unable to control such situations, but who are usually as perverted as the former."

Claudio smiled and explained:

"When I use the word 'perverted', the purpose is not to judge our brothers and sisters who temporarily dwell in the darkness. I merely want to qualify, for the comprehension of those who just recently arrived from the physical life, the situation of these sick friends. In fact, we consider them to be as sick as our mentally alienated brothers and sisters in any asylum down on the earth, and they deserve the best care we can give. With utmost respect, we know that large numbers of fathers, mothers, husbands, wives, children and loved ones of the spirits roaming these gloomy regions reside here due to pure dedication, working as anonymous heroes in an admirable apostolate of love and self-denial on behalf of those who harden their hearts in wrongdoing so as to help them recover their necessary balance and prepare for the new reincarnations awaiting them ... These models of goodness and patience might seem to be enslaved to the unfortunate ones they love, but because of their humble sacrifice they end up working miracles through the irresistible force of example."

Ambrosio's simple house could be seen in the distance, when Fantini showed that he wanted to continue on the subject:

"Brother Claudio, generally speaking, are there many spirits who are rescued by the loving dedication of those who watch over them in these places?"

"Absolutely. Each day our places of readjustment receive small or large groups of those who long for self-renewal."

"And do they stay in the city indefinitely?"

"No. With few exceptions, they stay with us long enough to prepare for a new reincarnation, in which they return to the disguises of the flesh, and without which they do not believe they can continue on the pathways of regeneration. Between the exhaustion of their mind's darkness while in the errant state and the terror of the spiritual light, which they don't believe they can endure without extensive preparation, they beg for help from Divine Providence, and Divine Providence grants them a new immersion in the physical armor. There, they can hide once again while struggling for their correction and spiritual growth, temporarily covered with the material body, which little by little wears out, revealing once again the good or evil they have done to themselves during incarnation. When they receive the loan of a new body, they are usually born alongside those who were their accomplices in the follies of the past, or those who are attuned to them through the same kinds of debts and resultant repayments. These candidates for expiatory recapitulation of the past beg for measures against themselves, either in a home environment that does not match their ideals or in the formation of the future body they will use. Many times they want some of its functions to be blocked, thus wisely inhibiting beforehand the inferior tendencies that led to their downfall in the past."

"Does this mean that they themselves ask for specific limitations for their own disadvantage?" asked Fantini with his usual sharp reasoning.

"Yes indeed. That is why there are great talents who are frustrated regarding the direction they would like their lives to take; astute minds that are barred from any academic accolades early on, forcing them to work as obscure artisans or to carry out simpler tasks in a lengthy and painful condition of subalternity, where they learn humility, balance, peace and moderation; artists who are frustrated regarding their highest aspirations, dragging around physical defects and other limitations that temporarily prevent the manifestation of their talents, but under which they will reeducate their impulses with necessary respect for the sentiments of others; women with an enormous capacity for love shackled to unsightly bodies, learning through terrible afflictions of the soul the pain of having deserted home and having despised the commitments of motherhood; dynamic and energetic men bearing insidious and hidden frustrations that keep them from the organic pleasures in the physical realm so that they can work on the spirit of understanding and charity in the core of their souls."

This enlightening explanation was received as an unforgettable lesson in the spirits of the listeners. It was suddenly interrupted by the greetings of Ambrosio and Priscila, who were waiting outside for the pilgrims.

Greetings, good wishes, blessings and joy.

The Gospel at Home took place next, displaying the same characteristics as the practice followed in the Christian homes down on the earth.

However, inside that simple abode invaluable spiritual support was extended to the suffering friends in the vicinity.

Longing for peace and transformation, twenty-two spirits – twenty women and two men – had come from the *great fog* nearby to hear what Brother Claudio had to say.

The tasks unfolded along the same patterns of the evangelical sessions down on the earth, supplemented by the well-known Christian Spiritist standards that allow for the respectful but free interpretation of the Lord's teachings.

Toward the end of the session there were passes[11] for comforting in addition to messages of clarification, advice and tenderness.

Ernesto and Evelina had an opportunity to serve, as their guide appointed them to soothe the suffering of two of the visiting sisters bathed in tears after hearing Claudio's remarks.

Outside the house the team was engaged in edifying conversation as they said their goodbyes to the humble attendees of the evangelical sowing, when out of the fog came a small group of scornful, demented spirits.

There was an explosion of swearing, mixed with derision and vulgarity.

Wishing to alert everybody, especially the two recruits, Claudio advised:

"Don't be concerned. This is normal here."

"You bastards! Get out; get out of here!"[12] roared one of the attackers in an uncommonly loud voice. "We don't want any sermons, nor have we asked for any advice."

When the volley of insults had subsided, Claudio stated loudly but firmly:

---

[11] [Passes are] a transfusion of energy, altering the cellular field. ... In magnetic assistance, spiritual resources are blended between emission and reception, helping the individual in need to help him or herself. A. Luiz, *In the Realms of Mediumship* chap. 17, International Spiritist Council. – Tr.

"Passes are the transmission of spiritual and psychic energies." (Emmanuel, Question #99, *O Consolador (The Consoler)*, International Spiritist Council, 1993). – Tr.

[12] We understand the inappropriateness of these pejorative quotes; nonetheless, although distasteful, we believe that the reactions of these unfortunate spirits interned in sanatorium-like or purgatorial regions must appear in the present account so that we may not evade the truth. – Auth.

"Brothers! ... For those of you who desire a new life with Jesus, we are your truest friends at the moment! ... Come and be truly free! Join us in Christ!"

"You hypocrites!" roared the same voice, followed by sarcastic laughter from many of the others. "We have nothing to do with Jesus! ... Impostors! You are just like us, only dressed in saintly cloaks! ... We are the ones who call you to freedom! ... Cast off your wings of clay! Crippled angels! Decked-out dogs! ... You are as human as we are! If you are brave, stop behaving like old mules muzzled by discipline and come and be as free as we are!"

That said, the mob advanced toward the fraternal group, but Claudio, obviously in prayer, raised his right hand and a ray of light crossed the short distance to the aggressors.

The throng of wretched spirits halted abruptly, terrified. Some fell to the ground as if traumatized by an uncontrollable force; others resisted, spewing insults, while others fled in a stampede ... Nevertheless, among those who were still standing, a young man cried out in an unforgettable tone of voice:

"Evelina! ... Evelina! ... Is that you? ... Oh! I'm alive; we're alive! ... I want Jesus! Jesus! ... Help! Help! ... I want Jesus!"

Claudio agreed compassionately.

"Come! ... Come!"

The young man tore himself from the gang, went in the direction indicated by Claudio, and in a few moments Mrs. Serpa, trembling and filled with consternation, found herself before Tulio Mancini, the same young man whom she had loved so much in the past, and whom she was convinced had been cast into the darkness of suicide because of her.

14
New Directions

Mrs. Serpa was stupefied, speechless.

"Evelina! ... Evelina!" the young man bellowed, almost insane with joy. "Now! ... Now that I've seen you, I know I'm alive ... Alive!"

Claudio realized the delicateness of the situation and ordered measures to be taken to accommodate the young man in Ambrosio's home so that he could start adapting to the new environment until suitable hospitalization could be arranged.

After receiving comforting passes to calm his emotions, Tulio Mancini was taken to the house of the modest couple, who welcomed him with joy. Meanwhile, the assistance group returned home.

A distinguished psychologist, Brother Claudio avoided any personal allusions, although he did tell Fantini and Mrs. Serpa that they would be able to visit Evelina's old friend the next day if they wanted to. He also promised to give them the address they would need, since he expected to settle Tulio into accommodations meant for readjustment and rest as soon as he could meet with authorities associated with his line of assistance.

Ernesto wanted to hear what Evelina might have to say about the suicide that had been the topic of so many of their conversations from the beginning. Nevertheless, he kept silent about it; he could see that she was obviously bewildered as she held onto his arm without saying a word. Conflicting thoughts raced through Fantini's mind, raising a lot of unanswered questions.

Wasn't Tulio a suicide? he asked himself. He had read plenty of informative literature regarding suicides after death, and he believed them to be suffering severe punishment for disobeying God's Laws.

So why had Mancini escaped due correction, wandering around as he pleased among rebellious and roaming spirits in the land of the mentally alienated?

However, he was a gentleman and stifled any comments and questions out of respect for the perplexity that had overcome Evelina, who had long ago won his heart.

Little by little, the team dispersed amid fraternal words and wishes of peace.

Once alone with Evelina, however, the ever-kind Ernesto tried to dissipate her obviously afflicted thoughts, smiling and talking to her cheerfully and infusing her with peace of mind and optimism.

"My dearest Mrs. Serpa, if we still had any doubts about the death of our physical bodies, which by now must have already rotted away in the bowels of the earth, we can no longer have any uncertainty from hereon out."

She tried in vain to smile. She felt crushed, worn out...

Ernesto redoubled his efforts to soothe her, and after a long series of constructive remarks, he concluded:

"Didn't we ask for work? Mightn't it be that, without realizing it, we were led by the local authorities to make tonight's discovery? This Tulio who was once the companion of your dreams may perhaps be the beginning of a new direction for us ... A new occupation, a pathway of access for our spiritual growth. You must agree that he is in complete need ... That tormented voice, those sickly eyes would not deceive us. This is someone who needs immediate care, and since he is someone you know, he is our nearest relative. We're the only family he has."

Because his friend referred briefly to the mixture of pain and astonishment the discovery had caused her, Fantini returned to his initial good humor and with open arms he joked:

"What better way could there be for Mrs. Serpa to start working?"

He planted his hands on his waist in a typical gesture and emphasized:

"As for the rest, my dear friend, I recall the philosophical saying of an old friend: 'Coexist and purify yourselves.' We are discarnate and need to grow morally now more than ever. If Tulio's presence is a call to the service that will test our capacity to love our neighbor, let's not hesitate to embrace this new obligation."

It was a few days before the two friends could see the young man again. He had recovered substantially due to the care he had received.

Ernesto gazed at him curiously during their first meeting, but Evelina was still surprised and troubled.

This was Tulio Mancini alright, but a different Tulio Mancini. He looked at her with piercing eyes, denoting peculiar sentiments. Neither she nor Fantini failed to detect his sickly intentions taking shape right there in front of them, although he couldn't grasp the fact that he was being inwardly observed and evaluated.

Without meaning to, Ernesto and Evelina exchanged impressions telepathically, realizing very clearly that they could communicate by using only the language of thought, especially here with someone who wasn't on the same level of ideas and emotions. They saw that they could read Tulio's soul as if it were an open book.

Taking note of the young man's enthusiasm as he thought he was still alive in the physical realm simply because he had met his ex-fiancée again, the two friends didn't have the courage to undo the delusion yet.

"What surprises me most is that I've put up with this doubt for so long," sighed Mancini, relieved.

With the clear intention of preparing him for the truth, Mrs. Serpa tried to change his line of thought by saying kindly:

"On my part, what I regretted most was that you shot yourself in an act of madness..."

"Who? Me?!" You didn't know?" asked the young man in amazement. "I did nothing of the sort! ... It's true that one day I was weak enough to try poisoning myself to death because of you, but afterward I realized that you didn't despise me and I wanted to win back your love at any cost. But it just so happens that, in his desire to get me out of the picture, Caio came to see me and asked me to go with him to my office so that we could discuss a book on International Law. He said it was urgent, so I didn't hesitate. It was a holiday and all the adjoining offices were closed. Once we were alone, he dropped his professional manners and started accusing me. He said that my cowardice at resorting to poison had shaken the love between you and him ... I tried to justify myself ... As I was explaining the purity of my affection, that bully spewed insults that I cannot forget. He grabbed a gun and shot me in the chest ... I fell to the floor and saw nothing else ... I woke up – I don't know when – in a hospital room, and ever since then I have felt sick and full of hate, trying to recover my health so that I could teach that bastard how terrible my revenge can be."

If a bolt of lightning had struck the three of them right then and there, it wouldn't have hit Mrs. Serpa as much as that terrible revelation.

In a flash she realized that Tulio had not left his body due to suicide; instead, he was gunned down by the man she had chosen to marry. At the same time, an astonished Fantini saw that the young man had been the victim of a crime unknown to the world. And whether it was because he harbored afflictive thoughts of guilt scourging his mind or because he could see that Tulio was obviously anxious to be alone with Evelina, he begged her telepathically not to make any effort to bring Mancini to reality, but to be patient until they could establish a plan to assist the unfortunate young man.

Mrs. Serpa understood and Ernesto asked to be excused.

He needed to think, to rest...

Furthermore, he stated, it was natural that the two had confidences to share heart to heart; they would all meet again later.

Although a bit displeased, Evelina agreed.

As she turned to her ex-fiancé, she felt somewhat vulnerable as if exposed to hidden dangers.

Mancini invited her for a short walk in the park of the institution that was housing him, and in a few minutes they were strolling slowly side by side among flowery bushes and protective trees, breathing the balmy breeze full of delightful fragrances.

"Evelina," he began, "who's that old man that's always glued to you?"

Evelina became painfully aware of the aggressiveness of the sarcastic question, but she answered kindly:

"He's a special friend, to whom I owe a lot of favors."

Tulio joked:

"You must understand that I suffered a lot trying to find you ... Now that I have, I won't yield your company to any other man, not even your father."

She was about to ask him to moderate his tone, but Mancini continued euphorically:

"Evelina, there's a world of things I need to know, to ask about and to hear from you ... I don't really know if I'm crazy. Where are we? What are we doing here? But I would rather talk about you and me, only about the two of us."

At that point in the conversation, they came across a beautiful, small gazebo completely covered by ivy.

In a supplicant voice, Tulio implored Evelina to stop there for a rest. He said he felt too much pain if he walked very far, that he had not been the same since he had been shot. Evelina obeyed mechanically, driven by compassion.

They sat down on one of the benches in the pleasant, rustic nook.

The young man glanced all around as if to be sure they were completely alone, and then locked the only entrance to the place, which received light and air through high, narrow windows almost as high as the ceiling. When he turned around and looked at Evelina, his eyes were filled with such passion that she shuddered.

"Evelina! ... Evelina!" he pleaded passionately. "You know I've been waiting for this moment of happiness for all these years of anguish ... You and me together!"

She wasn't completely indifferent to the appeal of that young man whom she had loved, and she was touched. She remembered the evenings of tender whispers in parks and movie theaters before she had gotten engaged to Caio Serpa. Yes! ... This was indeed Mancini, the young man that had impressed her so much: the same charm and the same enamored voice beckoning to her with a new destiny. Instinctively, she remembered her husband's unfaithfulness, his sarcasm dressed up in beautiful words at home, and for a moment her heart hung in the balance between the two, just as when she had been engaged ... Tulio was now right in front of her, promising once more an ardent and peaceful love ... She felt mesmerized by his words, but her watchful conscience called her to readjust her thinking. She felt dominated by a strange sentiment that attracted her to him; but, at the same time, something about Mancini was filling her with fear and a sort of repugnance. He was no longer the gentleman of days gone by. He was rash, insolent. Having recovered her mental balance, Evelina convinced herself she didn't have the right to give in to any circumstances incompatible with her dignity as a woman. She had married. She owed her husband loyalty and respect. Her conscience controlled her sensitivity. The notion of the commitments she had assumed guarded her noble, sincere soul. She gathered her strength and composure, resolving to remain in control of unjustifiable emotions.

While these thoughts burned in her mind, Mancini continued:

"Let me rest in your lap for just a minute! ... Evelina, I want to feel the warmth of your heart ... I need you like a man dying of thirst as he approaches the fountain! Have mercy on me!"

Aware of his inappropriate conduct, the young woman tried to withdraw and replied bravely:

"Tulio, get a grip! Don't you know that I married Caio, that I am responsible for a home?"

"Oh! That bastard! ... I understand that my long absence made you marry that criminal, but things will change; yes, they will ..."

After a short pause, he continued to say to the astounded woman:

"Evelina, I know you're not indifferent to my feelings! Come on! ... Tell me you understand!"

Then he tried to kiss her.

Although startled and frightened, she gathered her courage, and stepping back, reacted indignantly:

"Tulio! What is this? Are you out of your mind?"

"I've been thinking about you day and night ... Ever since I took a bullet from that scoundrel whom I shall send to jail, I've had nobody else on my mind! ... Don't you feel sorry for me?"

The moving tone of that voice touched the depths of her soul; nonetheless, Mrs. Serpa replied firmly:

"I understand your feelings and I'm grateful that you've remembered me, but do you think it's fair to assault me disrespectfully like this when I've told you I have a husband and must render an account for my acts?"

Mancini fell silent for a few seconds; then, in his staring eyes he revealed the anger that had begun to dominate the mechanisms of his mind. His tears turned to scorn and he broke down in a dreadful fit of laughter.

"A husband! ... A husband – that criminal!" he mocked. "The people I've lived with, the people from the *land of freedom,* are completely right ... I understand ... you are now among the saints, but I'm no fake. I am what I am – a man with his needs ... I want you and that shocks you? ... That's a joke! ... You're a woman like any other; you're no better than the ones I know from the *land of freedom,* the only difference is that you hide in the shabby disguise of self-control."

"Yes," sighed Evelina, hurt, "I don't deny my human fragility ... But don't you think that discipline and self-control are the best way to educate ourselves and dignify our sentiments?"

"Hah, hah, hah!" he laughed loudly. "Obedience is the straightjacket that hypocrites use to constrain the simple; but you'll change your mind."

The distraught woman entrusted herself to silent prayer, imploring help from the powers of the Higher Life.

Meanwhile, Mancini came closer, deriding her:

"Look inside yourself and you'll see your mask ... You're an angel with lead feet like all the other monkeys that wander around here in their costumes. Get off that! ... We are all free! ... Free children of nature to do as we please! ... Proclaim your independence if you don't want to end up in the slave house of the hypocrites that enslave us!

Mancini stepped toward her and was about to grab her, when providentially someone knocked at the door.

Although upset, Tulio immediately collected himself and opened the door.

The messenger promptly identified himself. He was one of Instructor Ribas' assistants and had come on his behalf to accompany Evelina Serpa to the Institute of Spiritual Watch Care in order to attend to an urgent matter.

Evelina sighed in relief and realized her silent petition had been heard. While she mentally gave thanks for her saving support, Tulio, followed closely by the messenger, returned to the house of readjustment, where he was taken to a special cell for those in need of isolation and treatment.

15
Time for Analysis

In answer to a request by Ernesto and Evelina, who were eager for an explanation with regard to the turmoil that Tulio's presence had caused them, Instructor Ribas made an appointment that they kept promptly.

Within the Institute's inviting atmosphere, the Instructor listened patiently to what they had to say.

"Why was Tulio so troubled? How could they – especially Evelina – help him as he needed? Would it be fitting to ask the Institute for any information concerning Mancini's accusations against Caio Serpa? Could they both take on the responsibility of helping the unfortunate young man?"

After hearing them out, their guide looked at them kindly and advised:

"You have repeatedly asked for spiritual work; don't find it strange if the time has come."

After a pause, he smiled:

"Tulio Mancini is the starting point for the redemptive work you have embraced. Search your hearts – especially our sister Evelina – and see what kind of pity his difficulties cause you. Where love brings balance, our conscience does not trouble us; where there is no guilt, there is no troubled conscience."

"Oh, Instructor!" Mrs. Serpa pleaded. "Please tell me what I need to do!"

"I will talk to you as if you were my own children, because there should be openness between parents and children."

And changing his tone:

"Sister Evelina, how did you feel when you were alone with our newly-arrived brother?"

Having promised herself that she would face the truth whatever the consequences, the young woman admitted:

"Well, when I found myself alone with him with nobody watching, I went back into the past, when I thought I had found in him the man of my life. I felt transported back to my youth, and then..."

"And then..." her benevolent mentor completed the reticent sentence, "your own vibrations encouraged his aggressive affection."

"But I suddenly remembered my commitments as a married woman and got a hold of myself."

"You did well," countered Ribas, "but even so, your heart *spoke without words*, triggering a new wave of the emotional maladjustment that Mancini experienced during his earthly experience, due largely to your unfulfilled promises."

"Oh! My God!"

"Don't fret about it. We are all indebted spirits before the Divine Laws, and we find ourselves in a period of significant transition, the transition from narcissistic love to selfless love. We have theories of sanctification regarding our sentiments, but in essence and in practice we are just beginners. In the sphere of noble thoughts, we absorb the influx from the Higher Realms, but in the ambit of inferior tendencies, we still carry the immense burden of demeaning desires that constitute strong appeals holding us back."

Impressed, Fantini commented:

"This means that the earthly human..."

"Is an intelligent being refined by abilities acquired along the road of evolution it has traveled for many centuries, but in general it is still wavering between animality and humanization, despite the special cases of some who are already on their way from humanity to angelhood. Most of us spirits still enrolled in the school of earth have switched from polygamy to monogamy with reference to sexual conduct. Hence the need for self-vigilance, knowing that sex is a creative faculty in the realms of body and soul."

However, showing that he didn't mean to avoid Evelina's specific problem, he added:

"It's understandable that you felt attracted as you did, Evelina, and your self-control is commendable because you called upon clear and responsible reasoning to curb your immature heart. No one reaches the port of inherent dignity without having sailed for a long time in the currents of life, learning how to handle the rudder of discipline. Therefore, we have to take responsibility for the errors we perpetrate concerning our sentiments in order to purify or redeem them at the appropriate time."

"I really am indebted to Tulio; I made so many promises in the past but left him empty-handed," sighed Mrs. Serpa, disconsolate.

"That's right. Tulio has committed many blunders up to now; even so, your conscience as a woman won't exempt you from your responsibility in the matter."

"How can I pay my debt?"

"By helping him cleanse his emotions, as one purifies the waters of a muddy well."

Noticing the apprehension that had come over the young woman, he added:

"Don't be hasty or forceful. We must accept ourselves for what we are and face the problems caused by our mistakes. We don't seek enlightenment in order to weep. You are perfectly aware of your role in our friend's moral failure. Let's take a calm look at what you can do to help him get back on the right path."

"Insignificant as I am, what could I do?" asked the Evelina humbly.

Ribas went over to a large piece of furniture resembling a complicated filing cabinet and took out a folder. He explained to Evelina that it contained a summary of the information she gave upon her first contact with the Institute. He then explained that, having studied the material she had provided on the events that had tormented her life, he had obtained supplementary information concerning the pathway she had chosen to tread. As such, he had learned that Mancini had in fact lost his physical body due to Mr. Serpa's criminal act, and that her husband had indeed deceived the human authorities with a perfect crime, which he skillfully made to look like a suicide. The victim of a premature discarnation, the young man, just like a sleepwalker, had aimlessly wandered around for some time on the earthly stage where the tragedy had happened. Some time later he had been taken to the same city of regeneration and renewal where they were now studying his situation. He had convalesced there for a few months; however, the passion that Evelina had irresponsibly inspired in his soul made her the object of his thoughts. Consequently, he had lost interest in getting better and ended up fleeing towards the dreadful zone of uncontrolled behavior, where he had surrendered to all kinds of follies.

Connected to the young woman who had needlessly promised him such dreams of blessedness and affection, he had corrupted himself in the land of darkness and had disregarded his own respectability. By returning to that resting place of consolation and equilibrium as a result of once again meeting the woman who remained in his mind as the chosen one, he had been granted a new opportunity at self-reeducation.

Mrs. Serpa and Ernesto listened in amazement to this exposition based on irrefutable logic.

Concerning Evelina's anxious questions as to what she should do, Ribas clarified:

"We can tell you, my sister, that because of your undisputable merit, your benefactors and friends in the Higher Realms prayed to the agents of Divine Justice not to allow your discarnation until you had begun your spiritual rehabilitation on earth itself. Thus, through the mental wave of your remorse in light of Mancini's supposed suicide, you attracted to your maternal womb the suffering spirit of a suicide who had been sentenced by his own conscience to go through the trial of a miscarriage in order to value with more respect the divine loan of physical existence. As we can see, the anguish of thwarted motherhood was extremely useful to you for having given you the opportunity to make a priceless reparation."

"But," said Fantini, "we were told that Mancini didn't commit suicide but was shot by his rival instead."

"Nevertheless," Ribas responded, "we should not forget that, driven by Evelina's behavior, the young man lamentably had tried to kill himself once before, thereby giving Serpa the model for the crime."

Smiling benevolently, he continued:

"We are among friends, examining the law of cause and effect. Let's remember that justice works within us."

"But…"

Surprised, Fantini hesitatingly tried to reply. He was unsure as to how to weave his new question in light of their mentor's obviously rational explanation.

It was Ribas himself who continued the thread of reasoning:

"We are automatically driven to people and circumstances that are in tune with us or our problems. By arousing ideas of self-destruction in the mind of a man whose attention she had won, Evelina moved from thoughtlessness to repentance when she realized his moral collapse in his failed conscious attempt at suicide. Only then, pressed by compassion, our sister understood that she had harmed the young man who had trusted her fully, and as a consequence she had harmed herself as well. By grieving for Mancini, she deplored herself, and in that state of negative emotions she became the vessel for a spirit in the condition she thought she had driven the unhappy man into. As a result, she automatically became the unfortunate mother of a suicide eager to expiate his own wrong. "

Looking kindly at Mrs. Serpa, he added:

"By unconsciously expressing the desire to exculpate yourself, your purpose reached the hearts of friends and benefactors in the spirit world and they obtained for you this blessed concession. So, before discarnating, you suffered the punishment you felt you deserved, anxious to free Mancini from the harm you had caused him. You didn't pay Tulio directly for the debt you had incurred; you paid it by helping a nameless suicide, as much a child of God as we are, thereby redeeming yourself according to the law that governs a clear conscience. As for the unknown brother, when he suffered the trial of premature birth, he began to repay a debt he had assumed regarding himself, learning how precious it is and how much it costs to be granted the treasure of a physical body as a tool for spiritual growth and progress."

Ernesto and Evelina listened in surprise.

"Eternal Justice works itself out within us," finished the instructor. "God neither condemns nor acquits us. Universal Love is always ready to get us back on our feet, to instruct, polish, uplift and sanctify us. Destiny is the sum of our own actions and always has predictable results. We ourselves are the cause of the situations in which our existence is framed, because we get from life exactly what we put into it. "

"What now?" Evelina asked astonished.

"Circumstances have brought your creditor to you because you, my sister, are luckily in a position to continue the restorative work."

"What should I do, my friend?"

"If you have really decided to renew your pathway, the time has come for you to help Mancini get rid of the sickly ideas that your behavior as an irresponsible girl planted in his mind. You can now be his dedicated tutor, helping him reformulate on the spirit plane his concepts of life."

"I can't be his wife."

Ribas patted her hand with paternal tenderness and replied:

"If a woman's wrongs were not perpetrated as a partner of a man's sexual life, she has no obligation to be his wife just because she owes him this or that compensation as a spirit; the same applies to the man with regard to a woman. Notwithstanding this principle, the law of love must be fulfilled, regardless of the forms through which love is expressed."

And speaking with profound tenderness he said:

"Right here you can regenerate Tulio's emotional state and sublimate your own sentiments towards him by supporting and teaching him as a maternal mentor. Almost always a person's recovery is like a delicate plant within the soul, which only grows because the selflessness of someone else cares for it with tenderness and the dew of their tears."

Evelina found herself bathed in hope. Fantini fell into deep meditation about the eternal realities, and Ribas, pressed by the schedule calling him to other departments, promised to continue the instructive conversation as soon as they had the opportunity.

16
Renewal Efforts

A new life had begun for both Ernesto and Evelina, but especially Evelina.

It was crucial to help Tulio, to bless him and to renew him.

To do so, the two friends registered in a school of preparatory studies for the highest sciences of the spirit. Radiating hope and enthusiasm, they began acquiring an understanding of evangelization, inner reform, mental connectivity, affection, aggressiveness, self-control, obsession, and reincarnation.

In order to speak constructively with the one she had misled, Mrs. Serpa was arming herself with as much instruction as possible about how to gain his understanding. Her most serious endeavor would be that of clearing his mind of the illusions that she herself had created. Fantini, on the other hand, had felt enormous pity for the unfortunate young man, and had received permission from advisors at the Institute of Watch Care to accompany her at a short distance, with the job of intervening if necessary.

On the day scheduled for the start of the task, which was to be subdivided into visits entailing instruction and nursing three times per week, Ribas personally accompanied the two workers to the mental health hospital where they were going to begin their new duties.

As a member of a small community of patients of the soul, the young Mancini was isolated in a solitary room, which the Instructor informed them was made of a material that insolated it against the impact of vibrations that might worsen Tulio's thirst for unseemly company.

The instructor introduced Ernesto and Evelina to the supervisors and assistants, and with everyone's encouragement, both got to work.

Tulio was delighted with Evelina's presence and continued to express his loving devotion in poetic words of tenderness and loyalty.

Mrs. Serpa, however, kept her guard up although she framed it with kindheartedness, praying for inspiration from On High so that she would not fail at the mission she had embraced.

Their *therapeutic dialogs* continued punctually. Nonetheless, Mancini refused to let go of the passion that absorbed him; he was like a boat stuck in the mud, incapable of moving away from the dock.

As soon as Evelina would begin to prepare the appropriate atmosphere for the lessons, he would start whining like a sick child, stating that he wasn't feeling well and that he was incapable of studying, that he felt like his dignity was being disrespected and offended. He would declare himself to be against any philosophical thinking, claiming that he wasn't the least bit interested in matters of faith. He insisted that he was strictly a *manly man* – according to his own definition – and as such he didn't want a nurse or tutor – even one as attentive as Evelina – but rather a wife, the woman of his dreams.

Evelina listened patiently to his unending sarcasm and complaining, deflecting his blows and clipping his destructive tendencies with help from Ernesto, who watched over her efforts with generous attention. Imbued with the new responsibilities that now underscored her life, and being a profoundly sensitive individual, Mrs. Serpa constantly focused on her husband, investing in him all the love she could. In her efforts to become Mancini's maternal tutor, she felt an increased need to be Caio's wife. Thus, she would think of Caio at every step, silently sending him the most beautiful thoughts of love. It was true that he had not been the ideal consort. Furthermore, she knew now that he was a murderer who had used all the resources of his intelligence to hide it. Evelina, however, was as human as any other person and always reminded herself that he had become a criminal only because he had loved her. In a dreadful act to win her heart, he had eliminated Tulio. She longed to see him again, to feel the warmth of his presence in order to reinvigorate herself for the moral battles she had taken on. Even so, no matter how often she and Fantini requested permission to visit their families, they always received the same answer from their mentors: "It's still too soon."

So, they tried to find comfort in study and work.

From time to time, they exchanged confidences.

Ernesto spoke tenderly of his wife Elisa and his daughter Celina. In his longings he saw them as crystal-clear mirrors of love in which he delighted to see himself, although Celina often treated him with cruel defiance ... Of course, his widow and daughter were not up against any significant financial problems. Fantini had bequeathed them considerable assets: a nice house, money invested in honest hands to provide them with a solid pension, and insurance coverage to tie them over.

But ... what about his absence? he constantly asked Evelina, who had become his constant, trusted sister. The absence, the distance!

The two would ponder circumstances down on earth for a while in an attempt to taste beforehand the joys of the reunion. They had been informed that there was now a *wall of different vibrations* between them and their loved ones. Consequently, they wouldn't be able to get their attention in the same way as if they were returning from a trip. It was their duty now to conform in the face of any changes they would embrace. Along such lines they had heard the most varied accounts of *the dead* returning from the earth depressed and sad because they couldn't be seen, heard, acknowledged or touched by their family members. Many did return consoled and hopeful as if freed from the ties and shackles that had weighed so heavily on their hearts, whereas others returned disappointed and sullen, in no mood to talk about it. They referred to friends and drastic changes at home, mentioning disasters and failures of their unforgettable loved ones in the realm of sentiments. Even so, the two of them remained optimistic and trustful. Evelina was enthusiastic and displayed her noble feelings, while Ernesto listened attentively. In her opinion Caio had fallen into error; however, he had redeemed himself to some degree because of the tenderness and selflessness he had displayed during the last days of the disease that had claimed her body. Yes, it was true that he might have been unfaithful for a while. After all, he was a man with the natural demands of physical life, and of course he would have enjoyed himself while he waited for her to heal. But once faced with her death and their long separation, he had changed and seemed to have recovered his stance as the loving, tender husband he had once been ... And Evelina, contemplating him with the eyes of her imagination, believed him to be forlorn and unhappy, anxious to be freed from the flesh in order to hold her again in his arms. She anticipated scenarios, while Fantini listened attentively to her sweet hopes. Rationalizing her assertions, she would state that Serpa had even gone so far as to commit the insane act of killing Tulio with the intent of marrying her – which, of course, had turned into an awful tragedy. Nonetheless, down deep Evelina showed unmistakable traces of the vanity of feeling loved ... She would declare resolutely that just as she was now making efforts to help Mancini, she would devote herself later to Serpa in the same way. She would do her very best to help him with any reparation he might need.

Then, Ernesto would take his turn in narrating stories from home. He loved his wife deeply and would confess to having made many mistakes when younger in order to keep the peace. And his daughter? Celina was a gift – always so tender, understanding and dedicated – someone who had comforted his soul in adulthood. He had dreamed of her finding a good, kindly husband, but he had left her when she was twenty-two, with no marriage prospects. In spite of his suffering as a father far from home, he had the greatest confidence in his daughter. He did not fear for her future. In addition to receiving a healthy pension, she was a fine English teacher. She earned her money and knew how to save it.

Many sentimental, nostalgic conversations unfolded along such lines between Ernesto and Evelina.

After six months of attention and instruction on Tulio's behalf, Ribas came to evaluate him personally as he had promised.

After checking Evelina's punctuality and efficiency through notes certified by the hospital's directors, Ribas entered the room and identified himself to the patient as a doctor making an inspection. However, he saw right away that Mancini had made little progress from his lessons.

Listless, he only had one thing on his mind: Evelina ... And with Evelina at the core of his deepest longings, other thoughts followed in succession: the yearning to make her an object that belonged to him alone, Caio shooting him, his desire for revenge, and the dark traits of self pity.

Ribas couldn't find in that anguish-laden heart the slightest crack to let in a single ray of optimism and hope.

At the first mention to his sentimental state, Tulio responded to the Instructor with the sadness of someone who knows his illness has no cure.

"Believe me, Doctor, without Evelina by my side I can't understand a thing. If I listen to the Gospel, I think that she – only she – is the angel who can save me; if I take notes regarding self-control, I see her in my mind as the only one strong enough to control me; if I hear exhortations to have faith, I end up wanting her to be my sole comfort; if I receive information about obsession, I finish the class confessing to myself that if I could, I would flee this hospital in order to pursue her and take her in my arms, even if I had to go to the ends of the earth!"

The mentor smiled paternally and suggested that he compose himself.

"Let's remember, my son, that we are eternal spirits. It is essential that we preserve our serenity and patience ... Happiness is an endeavor that takes time and God's blessing."

The young man retorted bitterly and irreverently. He had not asked for and would not accept any advice.

A skilled psychologist, Ribas said goodbye.

That evening he met Ernesto and Evelina and praised her efforts.

She had faithfully carried out her task of reeducating Tulio, but he hadn't responded constructively. He was apathetic, immersed in the fantasies he had created to his own harm.

Ribas finished by telling Fantini and Mrs. Serpa:

"I cannot see any advantage in keeping Mancini here. We must convince him to voluntarily accept miniaturization."[13]

---

[13] On the spirit plane, miniaturization or shrinking comprises the preparatory stage for a new reincarnation. – Spirit Author.

"To reincarnate?" asked Evelina, startled. "Is it that serious?"

And Ribas replied:

"Our friend is mentally ill – profoundly ill, traumatized, anguished, and taken by fixated ideas. The only solution is for him to start over. Even so, he will have difficulties and maladjustments ahead of him.

The benevolent mentor neither issued any warnings nor articulated any suggestions. Ernesto and Evelina, now engrossed in the imperatives and trials of reincarnation, became silent – thinking and thinking ...

17
Matters of the Heart

Ten months had passed since Evelina and Ernesto had started their assistance assignment with Mancini, when the two asked for a hearing with Instructor Ribas concerning some issues burning in their minds.

More than anything else, they wanted to see their loved ones on the physical plane.

Ernesto had become a well of memories regarding his wife and daughter, and Mrs. Serpa could no longer bear her homesickness for her husband and parents. Because they were so anxious to go back, they were eager for information.

Their mentor welcomed them with his usual kindness, and after hearing their request, he replied simply:

"I believe you're now ready for this. You have duly dedicated yourselves to your work, and you know now what reincarnation, self-discipline and inner reform really mean."

And demonstrating sincere concern, Ribas asked:

"Is there any particular, more intimately personal reason for your request?"

Somewhat embarrassed, Evelina answered:

"Instructor, I have missed Caio so much..."

"When far apart, husbands and wives start loving each other as if they were engaged all over again," Ernesto interrupted. "I must confess that I too yearn for my wife."

"Dear friend," ventured Evelina, gazing expressively at their mentor, "while we are on the subject of conjugal relationships, I would risk a question."

"Speak, my child."

"You're aware of the fact that when I met Mancini again for the first time I felt for a few moments like the irresponsible girl I once was, and I realized I was still strongly attracted to him. In order to fight that feeling, I found myself retreating mentally towards Caio, my husband in the physical realm, and I felt like a satellite orbiting between the two ... I started doing my best to help Tulio, and little by little I began to realize that he most definitely isn't the man I would want for a companion ... So, to help and tolerate him at present I feel the need for some sort of incentive."

"Love for God."

"I understand that we all breathe in the very essence of God, but this is a mystery to me ... I know we can't do anything without God, but between God and my duties I need someone to uphold my spirit, someone to support me in my daily endeavors as I search for that state of mind we call inner peace, euphoria or even bliss ... This spiritual hunger makes me think night and day about reuniting with Caio; could it mean that he, as my husband, is really my one true love? That one spirit who will be the sun of blessing to envelop me forever when we reach perfection?"

Ribas smiled and said philosophically:

"All of us are destined for Love Eternal, and yet, in order to reach that supreme objective, each of us follows his or her own pathway. For most individuals, finding ideal love is somehow like the search for gold in mines or diamonds in pits. You have to sift the gravel or sink your hands in the mire in order to find it. Whenever we love someone deeply, we make that person the mirror of our dreams ... We start to see ourselves in the person that we have made the object of our affection. If this person truly reflects our soul, mutual love grows more and more, guaranteeing us an atmosphere of encouragement and joy for the oft-difficult evolutionary journey. In such a case, we will have found a safe support in the ascent toward our moral perfection ... Otherwise, the person to whom we have particularly devoted ourselves ends up sending us back the feelings we project upon him or her, like a bank that ruins our investments due to mismanagement or the inability to safeguard our interests. At this point we are faced with the spiritual conditions we call bitterness, disappointment, indifference, disillusion."

"So, you mean to say," stated Ernesto, "that over the course of our existence we tread the pathways of affinity from one love to another until we find that unforgettable one who rises in our life as the flame of love eternal?"

"Yes, but we must understand the concept of love outside the limitations of sex, since the marriage union, although sublime, is only one of the manifestations of love per se. One particular man or woman may find in their spouse the ideal type; however, after marrying they may feel more intimately connected to their mother or father ... And sometimes they will find a stronger bond in one of their children. In love, affinity is what really counts."

"Instructor," asked Evelina, impressed, "what about marriages that are a torment, the unhappy ones?"

"Indeed, reincarnation is also recapitulation. Many couples in the world are composed of spirits who meet again to carry out particular tasks. At the start, their sentiments juxtapose in terms of affinity, like the cogs of two wheels that complement one another to make the mechanism of marriage work ... Thereafter, they perceive that it is essential to polish up other parts of this living mechanism so that it can produce the hoped-for blessings. This demands understanding, mutual respect, constant work and a spirit of sacrifice. If one part starts misunderstanding the other, or if both parts start misunderstanding each other, the work that had begun or re-begun will come to an end."

"And then?" Evelina's question floated in the air, filled with curiosity.

"Then the spouse who failed at the commitment – or both, depending on the cause of their disunion – must wait for new opportunities in the future to rebuild the love they squandered."

"Instructor, please allow me a question. If the conjugal union of two individuals who love each other is interrupted by the death of one of them, can it be restarted here?"

"Certainly, if the two truly love each other ..."

Fantini interrupted:

"And if not?"

"The one who loves sincerely continues working *on this side of life* to help the one on earth who does not have the same feelings. The former continues perfecting the sentiment of love in ways other than matrimony."

Mrs. Serpa's face lit up with a beautiful smile and she declared confidently:

"That won't happen to me. I now have enough reasons to trust Caio as much as I trust myself."

"Your faith," replied the Instructor, "is a picture of your sincerity."

Ernesto gazed at his companion for a long time and admired the tenderness of her good, innocent soul. For some time now he had been nurturing a deep affection for her. He had never caught her doing anything wrong; she was always compassionate and selfless. Sometimes he felt connected to her by an enchanting attraction. From what perspective did he love her? As a daughter, companion, mother, sister? He couldn't decide.

Afraid of letting his mind wander too far, Ernesto, good friend that he was, interjected with the clear intention of reining in his thoughts:

"Instructor Ribas, like Evelina, I too am sure that my wife is waiting for me ... But, what if she isn't?"

"If she isn't," and their mentor emphasized his words with a fatherly tone of good humor, "you will, of course, have the opportunity to help her as a fraternal friend."

"And in that case, would I have the right to choose a new partner in this realm?"

"Human laws, both in the terrestrial realm and here, are susceptible to being modified, and in essence they do not affect Divine Laws. On the earth, widowhood is not an obligation. Those who remain alone are free to do so. Once the bonds of marriage are broken with the death of the body, men and women alike remain on their own when they have reasons for it. It is only natural that the same would be the case here. The discarnate man or woman stays single or not, according to his or her inner purposes; however, we must remember that, in either case, there are resources to honor the efforts of building the pure love that will end up reigning permanently in our relationships with others."

Displaying a look of concern, Evelina sought more information:

"Instructor, do you know anyone who could not get married here?"

"I myself."

"Any special reason?" Fantini asked.

"It just so happens that, when based on pure love, conjugal love continues to vibrate at the same pitch between the two worlds without the exchange of energies from one partner to the other suffering any disruption. My wife and I have always been profoundly united. On earth we were enough for each other in terms of love. After my discarnation, I soon realized that she and I remained closely bonded as if we were integral parts of a circuit of energy. In her spiritual dedication, I find the means to continue my learning experience of love for all humankind; the same applies to her."

"An ideal relationship!" a thrilled Evelina rejoiced.

Revealing the anxiety that dominated her regarding her desire to be the object of her distant husband's tenderness once again, she commented reverently:

"Instructor, I've noticed that there is always some reservation when I talk to our more experienced friends here about the possible discarnation of the loved one's we have left behind ... I've come to think that this might be a forbidden topic. Am I right?"

"Not really. As our notion of responsibility increases, we understand reincarnation as a sort of 'school time'. Each lifetime is supervised by considerations of a higher level that are quite often incomprehensible to us."

Laying bare her inner longings, Evelina risked a question:

"My dear friend, suppose I find my husband missing me as much as I miss him ... tormented, sad ... Couldn't I encourage him in the certainty that we will be happy again here by promising him renewed joy after death? I say this because I didn't leave him any children to give him the courage to endure, to wait."

"You mustn't think like that. We have no instruments to measure the fidelity of those we love, and even if your husband were in tremendous distress due to your absence, we wouldn't be able to tell if discarnation would be the appropriate remedy for him. Who knows if a longer stay in the physical body wouldn't be the best thing for him in order to reveal himself to you with more certainty? To hammer the idea of death into his head would probably help him reduce the time of his material existence; and who can say for sure that he would be happy in returning to the spirit life because of our imposition and not because of a determination of nature, which is ever wise because it reflects the designs of the Eternal One?"

"Oh, dear God!" Mrs. Serpa sighed worriedly, "What can I do to help his heart which beats in mine?"

Ribas answered kindly:

"On many occasions, when we say that someone's heart beats in ours, it would be more correct to say that it is our heart that beats in theirs."

And even more kindly:

"In just a few days, Fantini and you can visit your homes."

Ernesto and Evelina thanked Ribas happily. A sweet joy suddenly bathed their souls as if their sentiments had moved from the mists of longing to the sunshine of hope in a new dawn.

18
The Return

At long last, the return.

Both Ernesto and Evelina were like children at a party.

The first trip home in two years.

Before joining the small group of spirits returning to their earthly homes in situations similar to theirs, Ribas gave them this recommendation:

"You represent our city, our customs and principles, so behave according to your new understanding. If you need help, get in touch with us through our mental wire."

Ribas embraced them and wished them a happy journey.

When the vehicle landed near the Via Anchieta[14], at the point where the road forks on the way to Sao Bernardo, the small group dispersed.

Each member of the excursion was an eager traveler, each of them a living world of homesickness.

---

[14] A highway between the cities of Santos and Sao Paulo. – Spirit Auth.

The group's director, also responsible for the vehicle in which they had arrived, scheduled their return for the next day; they were all to meet at the same spot in twenty hours.

Delighted, our friends breathed in the soft breeze that greeted them. They were surprised, happy; they could hardly believe they were actually on the outskirts of Sao Paulo.

They were overwhelmed with joy as they contemplated the clear, deep blue sky of a late afternoon in May. Around them, gusts of cool wind brought back memories of days gone by. They walked with joy enrapturing their hearts.

Yes, this was the city they knew; the place they loved ... They eagerly inhaled the aroma of the flowers and smiled at people in the cars that were going down to Santos that Saturday afternoon.

At a certain spot on the road, Evelina, whose heart and mind were fixed on her husband's image, stood in front of Ernesto as if he were a giant mirror, and asked with innocent tenderness what he as a man thought of the way she looked. She wanted to display the same simplicity and good taste that her husband used to want when he came home. She realized that the situation was different now, that he would not detect her presence physically, even though she could see him. Nevertheless, she had heard that people who missed their loved ones were able to see them with the eyes of the soul, as if they had a television screen in their mind. If Caio's emotions and feelings were focused on her, he would surely register her caresses, even if for him it would be nothing more than simple memories.

Ernesto laughed at her remarks and praised her perspicacity.

He looked at her hairdo and face, told her to smooth out the folds in her dress and approved of her shoes like a father encouraging his daughter on prom night. He then admonished her jokingly that it did not become her to be so coquettish.

The young woman justified herself, showing certainty of her husband's preferences.

Both were conversing lightly when they arrived in the Ipiranga neighborhood, where Evelina anticipated finding Caio in the same house that had been the theater of their happiness. Suddenly, her joy gave way to apprehension. As they approached her former home, she felt her chest tightening in a mix of joy and unexpected alarm. What if Caio hadn't been as loving and faithful as she had imagined? Doubt crept into her mind like a poisoned dagger piercing her innards.

"Ernesto, do you have any intuition about what is awaiting us? Can you believe that right now I feel terrified? My knees are shaking."

"It's the excitement."

"What else?"

Fantini looked at her very seriously and said:

"Evelina, do you remember what we tried to teach Mancini?"

"Of course! But what does that have to do with our problem?"

"Let's think. For months now, we – you particularly – have been talking to Tulio about matters of the soul ... Self-denial, understanding, serenity, patience ... Instructions given over and over, conclusions and repetitions."

"Yes..."

"Don't you think that with so many explanations about love and marriage, service and spirituality, Instructor Ribas wasn't doing the same for our benefit? Don't you believe that in conversing with us so thoroughly at times our devoted friend wasn't acting as a teacher looking ahead?"

"Yes ... yes ..."

"Let's be prepared for changes."

Evelina changed the subject. She said she was anxious, a bit tired. If possible, she'd like to rest for a moment. She didn't want to approach her husband with any signs of indisposition.

Ernesto proposed a few minutes of rest in the gardens at the Museum.[15]

They set out and stopped at the foot of a fountain. Its water seemed to possess the power to calm their thoughts.

As if he had been contaminated with his companion's fears, Fantini suddenly felt sullen. Just as he was about to see his wife and daughter again, his enthusiasm for the event was dampening. He became lost in thought. Evelina noticed this and started talking about hope and joy, reinforcing the merit of positive thinking. He registered the trustful words spoken by the young woman who had become his sister and friend, but was incapable of warding off the melancholy that had suddenly come over him.

Mrs. Serpa discreetly kept silent, but finally said she was ready for the last leg of the trip.

Gentleman that he was, Fantini promised to assist her during her first contact with home. She should check out the domestic environment first. If everything confirmed her optimistic expectations, she should return with the news to where he would be waiting for her at a nearby spot. He would then leave her with her husband until the next day, while he would head for Vila Mariana, where he hoped to see his own family again.

Evelina agreed; she didn't like to be alone in this, nor could she do without his support.

It was 6:00 p.m. Evelina no longer saw the sky above Sao Paulo, or the rows of houses or the pedestrians. With her heart pounding, she approached her home. She crossed the front patio and touched the door, which was no obstacle to

---

[15] The Ipiranga Museum in Sao Paulo. – Spirit Auth.

her entry. Something was telling her that Serpa was home and she proceeded, trembling and terrified. She looked around. The living room was the same, except for a few changes in the furniture. On one side was her husband's narrow study with its curtains open. She entered with the reverence of someone who walks step by step through a sanctuary. The books were in order. Suddenly, beside a small vase of flowers she saw the photo of a woman. She inspected the walls, searching for the picture she remembered of herself, but there was no sign of it. She felt stabbed by negative feelings. Her mind went blank. Obviously, she had been replaced. She felt the anger ready to explode in a violent fit of tears, but she gained the strength to repeat to herself the words of the Instructor: "Behave according to your new understanding."

Upset, she went farther inside, and coming upon the small winter garden she herself had planted near the kitchen, she saw the unexpected love scene: Serpa and the young woman in the picture she had seen a few minutes ago.

Caio was holding the young woman's right hand between his own in a gesture of tenderness that Evelina knew all too well.

Between revolt and disappointment, she took a step back. Awful chills shook the fibers of her soul as if a strange lipothymia[16] had come over her, announcing a new death. She wanted to run and to reveal herself at the same time, to scream and flee to bury her immense pain in Fantini's chest; but she couldn't. Unperceived by the two lovers, she had no other recourse but to collapse in a nearby chair and compose herself. Conflicting thoughts crossed her mind.

Who was this unknown woman? Was she the same one who had tormented her spirit with little notes addressed to

---

[16] A feeling of faintness. http://www.merriam-webster.com/medical/lipothymias. – Tr.

Serpa, decorated with carmine-colored kisses? Caio had sworn his undying love during her last days at home. How could he justify breaking the vows that she had kept as treasures in her heart? To what kind of new bonds had Caio surrendered? Had he remarried or was he irresponsibly toying with others' feelings, belittling life? What did the future hold for her?

She looked at the two of them and was astonished at their indifference to her presence. For the first time after the great liberation, she could see that the physical senses are contained within strictly set limits: Caio and his companion often looked right at her without seeing her; she, on the other hand, was forced to see and hear them like any ordinary person for as long as she stayed there.

Mrs. Serpa was in agony. Despite the yearning to disappear, to flee, her emotions kept her from moving.

With a wounded soul, she noticed her husband addressed the other woman with the same look of love that used to be hers. And there was more. She recognized the string of pearls that he had given her as an engagement gift now adorning her rival's neck. She wept angrily.

Nevertheless, although Evelina's mind was filled with burning thoughts, she could no longer rid herself of the subtle connections with the teachings of the spirit city that had become her home. For that reason, she felt she was being evaluated as to how well she was applying the lessons she had learned from Ribas and other friends of the Greater World. She remembered Tulio, to whom she had repeatedly taught detachment from obsessive emotional fixations, and she had to admit that she herself was probably in a state of even more selfishness and embitterment. She resorted to prayer, was able to humble herself, and fighting against her feelings, she concluded that Caio deserved to be as happy as he pleased.

Little by little, she managed to compose herself and began to listen to their conversation:

"Vera," boasted the smiling attorney, "in me you have found a peace-loving, sincere man you can be proud of."

"And how do you explain that objectionable woman in your office?"

"Now don't be jealous! A lawyer doesn't choose the clients who come knocking. I'm a man of the people and cannot deny it."

"So you mean I don't have the right to watch out for our relationship?"

"Who said that?"

"The phone call I received from that meddler left me crushed; you should have heard what she said about you."

"If we paid attention to everything people say about us, life would be unbearable."

"But I can't stand it anymore."

"What do you mean? Stand what?"

The girl Caio had called Vera burst into tears. He drew her to him as Evelina watched in surprise, and after kissing her several times on the face, he whispered in her ear:

"Silly girl! Happiness isn't a flower to be watered with tears! Come now! I'm yours and you're mine ... What else is there?"

If only we were married, if only I bore your name, I could deal with these women who torment our life."

"Nonsense! You exaggerate everything. I've told you I'll marry you, and I mean what I say."

"I've been waiting so long!"

"And how long have I been waiting for you to solve your family problems? You can't expect me to put up with a crazy mother-in-law!"

"My mother is just unhappy. We can't abandon her."

"I've already told you. Put that old woman in an asylum. She's lived her life and now it's our turn ... We're going to Guaruja[17] today; I want to see the situation for myself.

The young woman wept copiously in response. While Serpa stroked her hair in an attempt to console her, Evelina made an enormous effort to drag herself away from there. She yearned for Ernesto's presence, for his company again. It was impossible to stay any longer in the home she realized she had lost forever.

Lacking self-control due to the overexcitement that dominated her, she yelled for her friend as soon as she was back on the street. When Fantini appeared, she threw herself into his arms like an inconsolable child.

"Ernesto, Ernesto! ... I couldn't handle it!"

Her companion guided her discreetly to one of the patio's benches, and sitting her down beside him, he listened as she told him the entire tale in between sobs.

Fantini felt sorry for her and tried to forget his own trepidations. He couldn't guess the reason for the tenderness that drew him irresistibly to Mrs. Serpa. However, the days in which they shared these grievous experiences together had transformed Ernesto into her unconditional friend. In listening to her he shared her pain and took her side, forgetting about himself. Moved, he tried to calm her down:

"It's fair for him to be like this, Evelina. Caio is young. You two weren't an older couple like Elisa and me. I believe he has a place in his heart reserved just for you, but of course he has the needs of a normal man."

"But the girl with him is the same Vera who wrote him the notes ... The same one! That proves he was unfaithful before our separation and continues to be unfaithful even now."

---

[17] Guaruja, a popular weekend destination for families from Sao Paulo, is known for its beaches. – Tr.

Stroking her hair in a fatherly gesture, Ernesto commented:

"I've been thinking ... thinking ... Don't you think death has returned us to ourselves and that God has given us selfless benefactors who have supported and instructed us so that we could face the truths that we are experiencing now? What did we do with our existence in the world? Was it a course in selfishness or a learning experience in selflessness?"

His voice was flooded with inner tears.

"Did you have a husband so that you could love him or so that you could make him an object of decoration? We talk so much about devotion while still chained to our physical body! ... Wouldn't after death be the best time to prove our vows? Mightn't now be the time that Serpa needs consideration and understanding more than ever before?"

Not so much because of the words but rather the tone in which they were spoken, Evelina felt compassion toward Caio.

On the screen of her imagination she began to see her husband in a different light. Caio was indeed a young man and the Lord's designs were keeping him tied to his physical envelope. How could she expect the unwavering love that he was still so far from attaining? She had been secluded in the spirit world for two years without having seen him at all. How could she criticize his behavior? And why condemn the girl? Hadn't she seen her bitter tears at his thoughtless and insensible remarks? Couldn't she perhaps see Vera taking her place at his side, receiving his halfhearted commitment and inheriting the afflictions that she herself had gone through?!

Fantini broke the silence and shook her from her thoughts:

"Remembering what Ribas taught us, I've concluded that our instructors sent you on this excursion so that you could learn how to forgive and ... who knows? Maybe that girl..."

"Maybe what?" objected Evelina in light of his reticent words.

"Maybe that girl is the person for whom you should ask the grace to be Tulio's new mother. We have been studying complex themes involving passion and restabilization, guilt and reincarnation, inducing us to think and think about it ... On the other hand, Ribas showed us what Mancini needs without making any suggestions. However, we do know the young man is in our hands now during this phase of readjustment after having lost his physical body due to being shot by Serpa ... Don't you think that Caio should restore him to the earthly experience with the devotion and tenderness of a father? And what better occasion than right now to practice what Jesus taught by loving the one you regard as your enemy, and making her an instrument of assistance to benefit the indebted man you love?

Evelina understood the scope of such considerations and fell into her friend's arms, weeping copiously and exclaiming:

"Oh, Ernesto! ... Ernesto!"

A few more seconds and a car could be seen leaving the garage with the couple inside.

Holding back her sobs, Evelina said that she had heard the two were heading for Guaruja.

As the young lawyer got out of the car to lock up the house, Fantini looked at his young companion and turned pale. Then, perhaps more deeply shocked than Evelina had been, he stammered, stricken with distress:

"Evelina! Evelina, listen to me! ... That girl ... that girl is Vera Celina, my daughter!"

19
Revisions of Life

The two discarnate friends couldn't define the astonishment that had gripped them.

In a flash, a bewildered Fantini remembered the beach house and immediately asked Evelina to get into the backseat of the car.

Bitter deductions deluged his mind.

So, this was the girl Mrs. Serpa had talked so often about! ...Vera Celina! His own daughter!

The car began to move as heavy tears streamed down his face.

As if to console him without words, his companion took his hand in a gesture of caring. She could sense his pain as a father. He looked at her through a veil of tears and said only:

"Do you understand my grief?"

"Compose yourself," whispered Evelina compassionately. "Now we are more like brother and sister than ever before."

A few moments after they had set out, the occupants in the front seat started making trivial comments regarding the trip until they both registered the influence of their invisible companions.

Suddenly remembering Evelina, her rival risked a remark:

"Caio, sometimes I can't help wondering if you're not still in love with the memory of your wife."

"What? That's ridiculous."

"I always hear the best things about her."

"She wasn't a bad person."

"But don't you miss her? Don't you still feel her in your heart?"

Caio laughed sarcastically:

"I have no desire to live with the dead."

"That's not what I mean. I'm talking about your natural grief for having lost her."

"You know that Evelina was already dead to me long before the doctor signed the death certificate."

"I often catch myself analyzing her picture ... That sweet face, those big, sad eyes ... You had to have married her because you loved her!"

"Yes, I did marry her because I loved her; even so, life must follow its course. First, passion; and then, very often ... a lack of interest later on."

"But won't you tell me exactly why you became disenchanted?"

"Do you really want to know?"

"Yes."

"Well, I always wanted to be a father, but Evelina was frail, sickly. I think she had bad genes. I didn't see her faults until she lost the baby. After she showed she was infirm and incapable, the marriage became too much of a burden ... In her final days the only thing she did was pray and cry all the time."

He laughed openly and said:

"The only way out was to invent trips so I could be with you."

The discarnate woman held on to Ernesto more tightly, seeking a support to brave such inconsiderate remarks.

Implying that she didn't want the conversation to degenerate into disrespect, Vera changed the subject:

"Caio, couldn't you and I dream of a home filled with children?"

He turned his head from the wheel and cast her a quick but expressive look:

"Depends."

"On what?"

"As far as getting married is concerned, that's going to happen. But think, Vera. The business of raising kids is no joke. Your mother's health bothers me, with her crazy behavior and her fits."

As if he had caught Ernesto's thoughts reaching him from the back seat, Serpa added:

"What can you tell me about your father?"

The astute girl immediately recalled that her father had died from the same disease as Mrs. Serpa, but afraid to say so, she lied intentionally:

"My father was a robust man of impeccable health. Always young looking, people often thought he was my brother."

"What did he die of?"

"He was operated on for some benign moles and wasn't as careful as he should have been. Before he had healed properly, he began digging in the garden, cut himself, got infected and died."

"Tetanus?"

"Yes."

"How was he mentally?"

"He was very intelligent and sometimes amusing just like you, although he took life very seriously."

"I imagine he must have loved you in a very special way. His only daughter!"

"Not so. Of course, he loved me, but he was a broker with many different activities. Always really busy, with almost no time to spend at home. He was a good provider from an economic point of view and worked hard so we would lack nothing, but as a father I can't recall one single day when he sat by my side to listen to me or advise me on matters of the heart ... And as a girl, I could really have used it, but..."

"Not even a couple of hours?"

"That's what he used to say, at least; I never could tell him anything, not even my problems at school."

Fantini listened, feeling humiliated, stricken, confessing to himself that if he could he would go back in order to be the loving, watchful father he had failed to be.

The dialogue continued:

"But you must have enjoyed your mother's love."

"Not at all. Very early on I discovered that my mother was irritable, despondent ... She liked to be alone, and although she has never denied me attention, to this day she tells me to make my own decisions in everything."

"Did she and your father have a good relationship?"

"Nope. The way I see it, my mother always seemed to merely tolerate my father, without loving him, although she tried very hard in his presence to act otherwise."

"Didn't the poor guy ever catch on?" asked Caio mockingly.

"I don't think so."

"What about your mother's mental problems? Isn't it due to the grief of losing him?"

"I doubt it ... As soon as my father died she changed dreadfully as if she had always secretly hated him. She burned all his personal belongings, smashed his pocket watch, tore up all his photographs ... Can you imagine? ... She didn't even want prayers said for him ... And she started getting worse and worse ... Now, as we both know, she refuses treatment; she wants to be alone; she talks to herself; she laughs, cries, complains and threatens silence and shadow, thinking she can see and hear the dead."

"How weird!"

Although comforted by Evelina's sympathy, Ernesto broke into tears. He registered his daughter's remarks as if he had not known her until now. It was true that he hadn't been a man that displayed affection, but it had never crossed his mind that he was detested at home. Was the young woman right? Why had Elisa become mentally disturbed? What might have happened during the years he had been away?"

As the two discarnates immersed themselves in a rigorous analysis of the circumstances, time went by and the car finally stopped at their destination: a simple house softly illuminated in the night.

Excited but cautious, Fantini got Evelina settled into a spot nearby. As had been the case with her, he too expressed the desire to check out the home situation by himself. Only after that could he decide about the feasibility of introducing her to his family circle. Vera's position next to Serpa didn't encourage Fantini and Evelina to go in together.

Evelina agreed. She would take the opportunity to pray, to reflect.

Moved, Fantini entered the house that he remembered so well.

In the living room, everything was exactly as he had left it: the worn table and chairs that he himself had brought from his house in Vila Mariana, the fishing gear, the china cabinet with old dinnerware, the simple pictures hanging on the walls ... He wept as he recalled the warmth of days gone by. A few feet away, he could see his daughter's bedroom, where she and Caio were chatting happily; but there, two steps away, he could almost touch the other bedroom where he had lain beside his wife so many times, breathing in the sea breezes.

The clock showed it was a few minutes past 9:00 p.m. What would he find behind that closed door? he asked himself anxiously. Elisa ill? Depressed?

He remembered what he had learned from his friends in the spirit colony and how he had been prepared to face any surprises. Then he prayed. He asked Divine Providence for strength. He wanted to see his wife again with honor and dignity. His daughter's allegations in the car suggested prudence, caution. He was not there to complain but to give thanks, to help, to do good. He was eager to serve.

With this attitude he crossed the threshold and found himself in the bedroom he had known so well.

He never would have imagined the scene right there in front of him.

Elisa was lying down ... her body very thin, her face deeply wrinkled and her hair much grayer ... Stretched out next to her was a discarnate man, the exact same one he had shot so many years ago in a jealous rage! ... He stopped short, terrified. In a flash he remembered the last time he had gone hunting with two friends, the time when he had triggered the remorse and suffering that followed him for the greater part of his life ... Yes, that man without a physical body was Dede, his childhood friend, rather, Desiderio dos Santos, the man he had murdered, whose shadow he thought he had removed from his house for good. Fantini blamed himself, taken with remorse, benumbed with anguish ... How could he confront this adversary, who was insulting him by lying in his bed?

Fantini wept inwardly, overcome with desperation. Instructor Ribas had had very good reasons for delaying his return. A few hours ago he had discovered that his daughter was

Evelina's rival, and now there, before him and next to Elisa lay his enemy, triumphant and in control.

Would he succeed in meeting the challenges that life after death presented to him? He was finally going to have to deal with the man he couldn't stand. Both discarnates would face each other exactly where and how they were right now.

Fantini was able to compose himself and took a quick step forward.

His antagonist looked at him sarcastically without a word, displaying the calm of someone who had known this time would come. To Ernesto's astonishment, his wife noticed his presence and let out a terrible scream:

"Damn you! Damn you!" She roared, obviously obsessed, in the dim light of the moonlit bedroom. Get out! ... Get out of here, you murderer! ... Murderer! ... Help, Dede! ... Help, Dede! ... Get him out of here! Get out, Ernesto! Get out! Killer! ... Killer!"

Caio and Vera broke into the room, terrified.

One of them switched on the light.

The girl approached her mother, who was screaming profanities. Vera held Elisa's head in her hands in a gesture of desperation and tried to console her.

"Mom, what is it? We're here; no need to be afraid."

"Oh! Vera! ... Vera, dear daughter!" the sick woman sobbed. "It's your father, that wretch!"

The woman held on to the girl like a frightened child and screamed even more loudly, giving Serpa the impression of a woman who had gone completely mad.

"Your father's here, that despicable man! I don't want to see him! ... Save me, for God's sake! Let's go back to Sao Paulo right now! ... Get me out of here!"

The tears poured in a sea of anguish from Ernesto's grief-stricken eyes. For so long he had nourished plans for this reunion! ... So many times he had imagined himself a bird far from its nest, eager to rest in its warmth once more! And now he had arrived as an unwanted guest, loathed by his own family.

"Elisa!" he begged.

His disturbed wife could no longer see his spirit body after the bright light had flooded the room; nonetheless, she could still hear his emotional, firm voice repeating its plea:

"Elisa! Elisa, listen to me! ... I have always loved you."

Then a conversation ensued between the two, although Vera and Serpa could hear only one side of it.

"Shut up, you bastard! It's a love I've always detested!

"Why have you changed so?"

"Because I'm now free to say whatever I please!"

"But when we were together..."

"I was the slave chained to her master."

"But you always said you loved me."

"Truth is, I always despised you!"

"Oh, dear God!"

"Look who's talking about God! A murderer!"

"Why are you being so cruel?"

"Dede told me you're nothing but a murderer."

At that point of the dialogue – so very strange to the two incarnates who followed just one half of it – Serpa became unnerved. Stating that he felt uncomfortable with the sick woman's hallucinations, he started searching the house for medicine to sedate her nerves.

Meanwhile, the argument between the obsessed woman and her husband continued.

"Listen, Elisa!" begged Ernesto in tears. "I don't deny having made serious mistakes, but they were all for you because I loved you so much!"

"Liar!" Elisa laughed between sarcasm and insanity. "From the moment you struck Dede, I started to like him ... We were unhappy every time you came home because we began living together even before you were even dead. And we've been living together ever since ... Look at this room! Dede is exactly where he has always been!"

Such statements were peppered with details that charity requests us to omit.

Ernesto was weeping while his discarnate adversary smiled at him in scorn.

Just then, Caio appeared with the sedative. Vera injected the troubled patient with it.

A few minutes later, Mrs. Fantini threw herself back onto her pillow, disfigured and drained.

Just as Ernesto was crossing the threshold to leave, Desiderio dos Santos, his enemy, jumped out of bed and blocked his exit, screaming terrible insults at him.

20
The Plot Revealed

"Scoundrel ... Murderer! ..." shouted the aggressor. "You're not going to get away with it after all!

He stood in front of Ernesto, and blocking his way:

"You thought it was enough just to kill me, huh? Truth is that by depriving me of my body, the only thing you did was to put me inside your own house ... I live here, and your wife is mine now!"

His sentiments elevated after all the turmoil he had gone through, Fantini implored:

"Oh, Desiderio! I'm so sorry! Please forgive me!"

"Forgive you? Never! Far from it! You shall pay me every last cent ... Wretches! People like you hide the blood of a crime under the cloak of repentance and believe you can wash it away with fake tears."

And mocking:

"Nobody dies. You criminals, you may cheat the world's justice but you'll be punished by Divine Justice! ... And Divine

Justice, in my case, resides in myself ... an avenging spirit, yes ... that's what I am ... And who would refuse me that right?"

The unfortunate man's own desperation prompted a flood of tears of hate, and weeping he accused:

"Despicable criminals! ... I lost my life, my home, my wife, my daughter ... and you expect from me a reward for the cruelty of those who took my life! ... You kill a man and yet expect him to kiss your hands? You take cover under the impunity with which the dirt of the grave conceals your wicked deeds, and you still want to be honored by your defenseless victims?!"

Ernesto was sobbing.

He fell down on his knees with folded hands in front of his former victim in an attitude of contrition ... If only he had known what bitter trials would strike his soul, he would never have tried to return home. He would have learned to tolerate the fierce longing for his wife and daughter, and would have adjusted to other circles of struggle! ... However, over the past two years of meditation and study he had learned that, within God's Laws, every spirit receives from life according to its deeds. He had understood that one cannot ignore one's own conscience and that the day of expiation and readjustment will invariably come to the guilty. With this in mind, Ernesto inwardly sought the support of prayer, asking Jesus to strengthen his shoulders to bear the cross that he himself had fashioned with his own wrongs.

As Fantini remained kneeling in the sand at the entrance of the house, gazing up at the star-filled sky, Desiderio continued:

"Coward! ... Get up and face the consequences of your wrong ... We are now two men in the same condition, without the mask of the body, as you wanted me to be more than twenty years ago! ... Where is your arrogance now, your false smile, your weapon?"

"Oh! Desiderio, I didn't know!"

"Well now you know that I'm alive, you despicable criminal!"

"Yes, I do," muttered Ernesto showing his suffering on his face, "and I beg God to forgive me for the evil I did to you."

"If there is a God, he's on my side ... You can't use God's name to protect yourself!

"I admit it ... but I beg you, Desiderio."

However, the words vanished in Ernesto's throat, suffocated by pain.

"You beg what?"

"Forgive me in the name of your love for Elisa and hers for you! ... I had no idea my wife loved you so much! ... I'm a reprobate, I know it well ... but I became a criminal because I had so much love for the wife that heaven had given me!"

His cold adversary seemed to be moved before that testimony of selflessness and humility, but returning to his characteristic hardness, he continued:

"Why didn't you choose a different way to get me out of the way? By using violence, the only thing you did was to push me more forcefully into your wife's arms ... And during the time you continued to live in this house after you thought you had killed me, I lived here too, sharing everything with you ... Whenever you thought you were seeing me only through the eyes of your imagination because of your remorse, you were instead really seeing me, Desiderio dos Santos, through the mirror of your conscience. Discarnates call me an obsessor spirit ... And what else could I be? I am what I am – a deceived man, the maker of my own revenge!"

"Oh, God of Mercy!" Ernesto lamented. "I'm guilty, the only one responsible ..."

The bitter persecutor gave a hearty laugh and retorted:

"No, no! ... You're not the only one ... You came up with the idea and the plan for the crime that snatched me from my physical life, but the true killer, the one who used your evilness to destroy me was somebody else ... I don't know why, but my fate lies between executioners! ... You're the one who tried to shoot me to keep me away from your wife, but when that wretch Amancio saw that you had missed, he took advantage of the situation in order to eliminate me and get my wife! ... You sinister friends ... you satanic companions ... who could have brought you together on that dreadful morning like two monsters to end my life?!"

In spite of the suffering that swirled in the depths of his soul, upon receiving this revelation, Ernesto recalled the dreadful day when he and his two companions had decided to go quail hunting. Desiderio, joyful and trusting; Amancio, preoccupied with the two dogs trained to find and fetch the prey; and he, Fantini, deep in thought, preparing for the crime. He remembered that Amancio excelled in handling the dogs and was completely engrossed with the success of the hunt. After a few short incursions into the woods resulting in wasted shells, Desiderio had climbed an old tree and had settled among its thick branches to shoot at the birds as they flew by. Amancio was on one side and he, Ernesto, on the other, with a small distance between them. When he saw Desiderio closely watching a bird gliding still too far away, he had shot at him and had run off terrified, hiding among the trees, waiting for the result of his unfortunate deed. He hadn't heard anybody scream, but instead, he had heard more shots, which he of course attributed to Amancio's gun in the course of the hunt. After two or three minutes, he had heard Amancio yelling for help ... He was terrified, in utter dismay; however, he dragged himself to the place where Desiderio's body lay in its final convulsions ... Deeply disturbed, Ernesto couldn't think of anything except his own terror for the mistake he had made, and thus he was relieved to accept the immediate explanation of his friend, who was crying out, "An accident! ... A terrible accident!" Wasn't that the ideal solution to prove his innocence? His hunting partner gave him a strange look as if wordlessly laying responsibility for what had happened on Ernesto while at the same time showing understanding and sympathy ... Suddenly, he remembered that the load had hit Desiderio under his jaw and had gone upward – something he had found very odd at the time. However, the circumstances didn't allow for an examination ... He took advantage of the confusion in his favor. Afterwards, his heavy conscience was soothed by people feeling sorry for him because they thought it had been a tragic accident. He had intentionally omitted all possible doubts that might have induced him to confess his crime. With a heavy heart, he remembered that after the victim's funeral he had broken off his relationship with Amancio for good under the pretext of grief. He had used all his strength to forget his victim's wife and little daughter, whose screams on that unforgettable day had smitten his heart, convinced as he was of being the only guilty party.

Terribly frightened, Ernesto realized that in seconds all the scenes of the tragedy were coming back to him on the screen of his memory, while Desiderio, as someone who could follow the innermost details of that compulsory retrospection, continued to insist implacably:

"Remember, you wretch! Remember how the two of you cynical murderers killed me ... How could I have left my motionless body without detesting you? Crazed with suffering and rebelliousness, I refused in disgust the merciful arms of nurses who came for me to take me to other lands, I know not where ... I was surprised to find out that life continued after death, and I wanted to use it only for revenge ... You didn't see me in my first days of furious hatred, although I still have enough reserves of fire and bile to pour onto your spirit ... Massive afflictions fell upon me; but you, supposedly a moral man, shall now receive in the court of your conscience the relentless power of my accusations as my greatest revenge!"

Desiderio went on in a mixture of cruelty and tears, repugnance and pain:

"Just think about the torment I suffered when, discarnate, I approached my young wife and my little girl again, only to see that murderer Amancio had taken over their lives ... Ah, Fantini! Do you think in the beginning I wanted your wife so badly? No! ... I was a man without any religious principles, and, consequently, without a defined set of conduct. I had a wife and a daughter whom I adored, and I had eyes for Elisa only in the sense of a fool that flatters himself at the attention he receives from such a devoted and distinguished woman ... However, instead of an open friend to friend conversation, which would have put me in my place, you were pierced with raging jealousy and tried to kill me like an animal in the field ... In doing so, Ernesto, you only turned me into a beast without its cage of bones. Loathing the intruder in my house – because Amancio wasted no time in marrying Brigida, the young woman I had left behind, widowed and inexperienced – I felt in my old home a hell that kept pushing me out ... Beaten like an unwanted dog, without the wife who had erased me from her memory, and without the daughter who now had to treat my executioner as a second father, I wandered aimlessly on the roads of despair among the mobs of darkness until I finally settled next to your Elisa, whose silent tenderness called to me insistently ... Little by little, from the point of view of the spirit, I adjusted to her like a foot to the shoe, and I began to love her fervently because she was the only person on earth who kept me in her heart and memory."

When Desiderio paused to rest for a moment, Ernesto wanted to beg for mercy, but he couldn't; the words got stuck in his throat, muffled in despair, while all the inner fibers of his soul trembled. He felt like a condemned prisoner hearing his sentence without any possibility of defense.

Fantini's adversary had recovered and attacked again:

"And why was that possible? Because remorse had distorted your mental health ... after the crime in which I lost my body, you began incessantly seeking an impossible way out ... You immersed your mind in business and profits, commitments and brokerages, traveling and traveling without trying to find out if your wife and daughter were in need of attention and love! All of this made my affection for Elisa more than an earthly affection. Obsessor? Oh, yes, I am ... but I am also an unconditional servant of someone who carries your name and who suffered the coldness of your heart ... I learned with your wife the patience and silence to wait and wait ... Were you ever aware of the illnesses your daughter had during childhood? Did you know about her difficult temptations as a young woman? Did you find out about the insensitive young men who abused her trust? Did you, by any chance, ever see the hot tears that burnt her face after being spurned by those same cynical young men that had promised her tenderness and loyalty? Ah! ... Fantini ... Fantini! ... You never took part in the torments that befell your home, but I know what sufferings were endured by one woman, who grew old in grief, and by the other, who grew up in tears! ... By what rights have you returned to this house? To reap the love you didn't sow? To demand an accounting?"

Broken with sorrow by what he heard, Ernesto managed to stammer:

"Oh! Desiderio! ... Now I see ... Forgive me!"

Ernesto's antagonist, ever more angered by the moral ordeal obvious in each sentence, continued his accusations:

"I suffered for your daughter and for the other, the little one that death forced me to leave behind ... Deceived by the trust she had in the rascal that had grabbed her attention, Brigida agreed to get rid of our little daughter, sending her too early to boarding schools, where she received a fine education, but suffered the lack of parents as if rejected at birth ... How I suffered, Fantini! You can't imagine how I suffered! But my troubles weren't over yet ... My poor daughter, who grew up sad and almost unprotected, deprived of the paternal assistance that Amancio and you stole from her, found death exactly two years ago ... Encouraged by her stepfather, who wanted to free himself of the responsibility of her custody, she married too young to a wretch who killed all her dreams ... Oh! How hard I tried to warn her not to marry that coward ... I went constantly back and forth between your family and mine, crushed by despair, dedicating myself to preventing the tragedy that finally took place ... When she died, I went to see her, together with a group of discarnate spirits as unfortunate as I was. I knelt down in front of the motionless body that still retained her last smile, and I swore revenge on the three deceitful faces gathered around her – Amancio, the killer, Brigida, the ingrate, and the detested son-in-law whose presence makes me sick! ... In tears I asked God for the grace to see my daughter delivered from her physical suffering and the fortune to hear her voice. However, compassionate spirit nurses told me she had been taken to a resting place and that I would only be able to see her again after having shed the hatred that I feel inside, as if it were possible to put out the fire of anguish that burns in my tormented mind! ... My poor daughter! ... She married a criminal as if she had to share my fate as a lost soul ... And now ... How to extinguish the flames of the bitterness that devours me? Impossible!"

Ernesto was sobbing.

Giving the impression that he wanted to pour out the sorrow in his wounded soul all at once upon his miserable friend, Desiderio continued:

"But you need to hear more ... Realizing that my daughter was deteriorating and feeble due to the disappointments of her marriage, her husband set out for new adventures and ran into Vera Celina, your daughter, and won her love ... Then he dominated and enslaved her."

And pointing with his finger toward the interior of the house, he added:

"That criminal is in there right now ... His name is Caio Serpa ... Evelina! My daughter! ... Evelina!"

As soon as Fantini heard Desiderio say the names of Evelina and her spouse, the whole story came together. He felt as if his brain was about to explode in raging agony. He jumped up abruptly, and although asking for Jesus' blessing and Ribas' protection, he ran toward the nearby woods, barely concealing his screams, and threw himself on the sandy ground of the isle like a dog yelping in pain.

21
Return to the Past

Ribas' warnings and Evelina's presence nearby were reason enough for Fantini to regain his self-control.

After getting over his long, tearful outburst and his surprise at finding out about Mrs. Serpa's new standing in his life, Fantini felt like a new man. He had gone through a transformation in the innermost workings of his mind. Desiderio's honest and straightforward account had forced him to face the extent of his weaknesses, a process that had not only rid him of his pride but had also cleansed his soul, giving him a new lease on life. Feeling somewhat shaken, he got up off the ground nevertheless and dragged himself to where the young woman was waiting.

Evelina was engaged in friendly conversation with some un-well discarnates who were visiting the area under the watch care of attentive nurses in order to benefit from the nourishing emanations from the sea. When she saw her friend staggering toward her she ran to meet him.

"Ernesto! Why are you so exhausted?" she exclaimed in concern as she helped him sit down on the sand.

He readily accepted her support, and as soon as she sat down beside him, he put his head in his hands like someone finding it difficult to put his thoughts in order, and stammered in tears:

"Evelina, Evelina! ... I now know that we are among the dead who have never received prayers from the living ... The hearts of those I used to love the most were closed off forever with the headstone that sealed my remains for good ... I'm returning from my home as a villain! ... Oh, God! ... Oh, dear God!"

His companion tried to comfort him as she recalled her own experience of a few hours ago, but her disconsolate friend replied in profound grief:

"No! No! ... You were a victim of ingratitude, whereas I received the condemnation I deserved ... You were merely insulted; I was actually punished!"

Ernesto was anxious to tell her what had happened, to share the revelations that had come his way; but his strength was faltering. Only tears flowed in waves.

A few minutes later, however, their confusion and affliction lessened with the arrival of the special flying vehicle that had come from Via Anchieta to Praia do Mar Casado[18] in order to take them back to Sao Paulo.

Ribas had heard his tormented student's desperate pleas and had expedited urgent orders for the Institute of Watch Care's two wards to receive immediate help.

Evelina gave her arm to her companion and helped him get into the vehicle, which then ascended. However hard she tried to get him to talk, he only responded with a few terse words.

[18] A Brazilian beach outside Sao Paulo. – Auth.

Fantini fell silent, his bewildered eyes revealing the turmoil of the conflicting sentiments exploding in his chest.

After a few minutes of flight, and heeding Ribas' instructions, the two travelers were admitted to the Resting Section of one of the Christian Spiritist centers that grace the city of Sao Paulo, where Ernesto began to receive the care he needed to recover from his trauma.

Appropriately treated by means of magnetic resources in a circle of prayer, he calmed down with the assistance of his companion, and only then, with his energies re-harmonized, did he ask her in a tone of infinite sorrow:

"Evelina, was your father's name Desiderio dos Santos, and is your stepfather Amancio Terra?"

"Yes, my full name is Evelina dos Santos Serpa."

Ernesto didn't hesitate. He realized he owed the young woman a full confession of his life, and getting down to it, he started by recalling his marriage to Elisa. Before Evelina's astonishment, the scenes from the past began to unfold one by one, albeit brushed in lighter tones: his close relationship with Desiderio since childhood; his superficial acquaintance with Brigida, whom he had seen only a few times; his friendship with Amancio, who had remained single; Desiderio's frequent visits to his house, which he, Fantini, never reciprocated; the attraction Desiderio exerted over his wife, whom he had loved so dearly; the jealousy he felt at seeing them drawn towards each other; his plan to kill the friend he had come to hate; the silent anger that had poisoned his sentiments; the sinister hunting expedition, the intentional shot and the other shots he had heard; Desiderio's death and the remorse he had felt his entire life ... And finally, step by step he described all the details of his return home, from the moment he had first heard the obsessed Elisa's accusations up to Desiderio's last statement, which had left him utterly destroyed.

Evelina tried in vain to find words to describe her amazement. Not that these disclosures would drive her from her friend, to whom she devoted a respectful and tender love. What was a puzzle to her was the complex drama of which they were the protagonists without even having realized it and the surprising twists and turns of the play the group was acting out. Moreover, she felt utter compassion for the internal conflicts of all her co-actors in this family tragedy. She realized that of all of them she had been hurt the least.

She looked at Ernesto and wept.

Noticing her silence and the dignity with which she suffered the pain that seared her soul, Fantini asked her anxiously:

"Aren't you going to accuse me too?"

"Oh, Ernesto! Each day our friendship grows deeper ... I'm the one who must ask you to forgive my father for having usurped your home."

Fantini replied, moved even deeper:

"No! He stole nothing ... He protected the wife and daughter I had forsaken ... And when it comes to apologies, I'm the one who should be asking for forgiveness for my daughter stealing your husband."

"No! No!" It was Evelina's turn to defend the girl. "I can see now that Vera crossed my path as a benefactor; she gave Caio the security that I couldn't."

"Evelina," her companion pointed out somewhat relieved, "I now believe that only through life after death can we undo the terrible mistakes we make during our stay on the earth."

She agreed and they continued in tender understandings until Fantini finally fell asleep, giving her the opportunity to leave him alone for a brief rest.

Dawn was setting in.

At the time agreed upon, transportation arrived to take them back to Nosso Lar.

Mrs. Serpa was dying to see her father again; her friend, however, thought it prudent not to do so without better preparation. Both were feeling much better and almost totally recovered, so much so that, like the other passengers, they discussed the fundamental themes of existence, such as love, reincarnation, home, and the need to suffer.

Back in the colony, they continued dreaming about the future. Together they talked; together they planned.

Wouldn't it be highly desirable for Tulio to be re-born to Caio and Vera, whose marriage they should support? Kind as always, Evelina remembered her suffering father and pointed out that if she were permitted and circumstances allowed, she would love to help her rebellious father accept a new reincarnation in order to forget ... in order to put the past behind him ...

She and Fantini were surprised at how they wanted to dedicate more and more time to their loved ones. They would pray for them. They would beseech God to prolong their lives in the physical world for the sake of both the family group and the two of them. Mrs. Serpa dreamed of seeing Mancini in Caio's home for their reconciliation, and Ernesto agreed that it was crucial to analyze the suitability of a meeting between Amancio and Desiderio so that aversion could become sympathy and discord unity. They dreamed and dreamed.

Ten days after their first return to Sao Paulo and after both felt completely recovered, they asked for a hearing with Ribas in order to expound their new ideas and to tell him about the latest events.

Their mentor greeted them with his usual kindness and listened attentively to their plans; however, to their surprise, he summed up the responses that both would have preferred to be longer:

"Dear friends, when Fantini's prayers reached us, we not only sent the help he requested, but we also asked for the records of all the family events involving your participation. Through appropriate documentation, we now have all the information you received. As for our moral duties, we have already discussed them sufficiently during our extended interviews; we know just what to do. It's obvious that we have reached the point of active spiritual work, which, by the way, you have requested many times."

"Will it be OK if we continue to work on behalf of our families?" asked Ernesto, sincerely wanting to do the right thing.

"That is our duty, my friend," stated Ribas. "Those who know must help those who do not; and not only help, but help with love."

"Could we perhaps see my father and Mancini reincarnate in the near future?" asked Evelina shyly.

"And why not, dear child? But in doing so we must establish concrete data, with precise planning. Of course, we are all one single family before Divine Providence, and we are all interconnected with the duty of mutually helping one another. Evolution is our long journey back to God ... Those who love the most are the ones leading the way, pointing out the path to their brothers and sisters."

"We would like some guidance, some advice on how to start," said Fantini, showing his concern not to impose.

Their guide summarized:

"Our reports are ten days old by now. I'll send an impartial observer to Sao Paulo today to determine the overall condition of all the brothers and sisters involved in this case. As for the two of you, tomorrow you can go to the south of Sao Paulo to contact the rest of the family members you haven't seen yet. Upon your return tomorrow evening, we'll start our examination based on more updated and accurate information."

The meeting was over.

The following day, using the regular transportation from the spirit colony to the physical world, the two friends arrived on the outskirts of the city, where Amancio had built his home.

Accompanied by Ernesto, who had become her brother and inseparable supporter, Evelina crossed the threshold of her old home.

It was a sweet return to her childhood days. She felt she was returning home hungry for affection, just like during her youth at the start of summer vacation. Over there, the plentiful orchard; here, the gate covered in wild ivy ... A few steps further, the huge courtyard extending toward the wide squares used for processing coffee ... Supported on her friend's arm, Evelina walked up to the front door under the power of the memories flooding her soul ... She went into the house with the tenderness of someone entering a place deeply sacred to the heart ... The same atmosphere clothed in peace; the parlor with that same old furniture that spoke so loudly to her memory; the wall clock that her mother was so proud of having received from her grandparents; the animal skin rugs, souvenirs from Amancio's many hunting expeditions to Mato Grosso[19]; the five-lamp chandelier hanging from the ceiling, and the piano on which she had so many times ecstatically watched her mother's agile fingers playing Chopin.

A surprise immersed her in joy. On top of the instrument, next to some forgotten compositions, she saw a photograph of herself as a young woman and next to it a faded rose that symbolized her mother's love for her.

She hurried to the side porch, where Amancio and his wife used to rest after meals, and there she found them sitting in their armchairs talking quietly. Overcome with indescribable emotion,

---

[19] Brazilian state containing an area called Pantanal, one of the richest ecosystems in the world. It is no longer a hunting destination. – Tr.

Evelina knelt before her mother, whose face was covered with more wrinkles and framed by more locks of gray hair. Putting her head on her mother's knees, she wept convulsively, as she used to do during the troubles and whims of childhood.

Dona Brigida couldn't feel her presence directly; however, she rested her pensive eyes on a tree nearby and suddenly felt an indescribable longing for her daughter. Tears pooled in her eyes without falling. "How I wish I could see my dear Evelina again!" she thought. Evelina could read her thoughts and answered: "Mom! Dear Mom, I'm right here!"

After a few minutes of silence Amancio, observed curiously by Ernesto who examined the damage that time had inflicted on him, looked questioningly at his wife and asked:

"Why so quiet all of a sudden, my dear? What are you thinking about?"

His voice carried the kindness typical of a man who does not let his devotion to his wife wane after marriage, surprising Fantini with his tenderness.

"I can't explain it, Amancio," answered Brigida, "but I've been missing our daughter a lot lately ... She's been gone for two years now."

And more emphatically:

"Why did she have to go so early in life?"

"Oh, Brigida!" objected her husband with remarkable devotion. "What cannot be changed should be forgotten; we can't undo the past."

"But I believe there is another life where all those who loved each other much in this world will meet again."

"Philosophers say there is, but practical people rightly believe that we know nothing about the dead except their death certificate."

At that moment Ernesto placed his hand on Amancio's head as if to read his concealed thoughts. Carved in Amancio's memory, he identified the living scenes of Desiderio's murder deeply locked in the compartments of his mind. However, something told him deep down that it wouldn't be advisable to induce Amancio into a negative state; that would be inappropriate at this juncture when everything led him to believe that Amancio had become the source of respectable work for several families.

Ernesto saw Amancio not only as a dedicated and tender companion for the woman who had been his victim, but also as an esteemed and honorable administrator, judging by the large number of peaceful and contented employees around the place.

Moreover, he thought, how could he accuse Amancio if he, Ernesto, hadn't killed Desiderio only because of his aim was off? Before God and his own conscience wasn't he as guilty as Amancio, who had had the misfortune of hitting his target?

Such thoughts were burning in his mind when he heard Evelina tearfully pleading to her mother:

"Oh, Mom! My father is wandering around in the darkness of the soul! ... He has become a spirit hardened in hatred ... What can you and I do to help him?"

Up to this point Brigida's mind had been far removed from any concern for her first husband and it couldn't register anything directly except a vague, painful urge to return to the past; but it wouldn't allow Desiderio's image to intrude on her memories. Still, her daughter insisted:

"Mom, please help Dad so that he can return to life on earth! ... Who knows? ... You and my father Amancio are living all alone in this house! ... What about a boy ... a son of your heart!"

At this point of her daughter's appeal, Brigida let the idea form in her mind that she and her second husband were growing old with no descendants, and that an adopted child could perhaps be a means of support in the future.

Influenced by Evelina's words, her thoughts grew in that direction and she began to reflect over and over ... A son! ... Someone who could fill her life with new hope, someone who could continue to uphold the ideals of work in that small corner of land!

Moved by her daughter's enthusiasm as she assimilated her thoughts soul-to-soul, Brigida probed her companion:

"Amancio, I often think about our growing old by ourselves, when there are so many possibilities ... What would you think about us adopting a baby boy to be the child we never had?"

"What an idea! At our age?"

"We're not that old."

"Oh, come on, Brigida! Don't you think it would be weird for us to finish our lives filling baby bottles?"

"What if it's just the opposite? God may grant us a long time yet ... What if we left behind a strong young man to look after the farm and continue our work?"

"I'm not so optimistic," answered her husband with tenderness and love filling his voice, "but I've always admired your whims. I have no objection to your desires, but the child would have to be a baby boy who would come here right after being born, without his parents bothering us ... and one who doesn't cry a lot ... and only if you don't complain about the extra work."

"Oh, Amancio! How happy I am!"

In light of his wife's transfiguring contentment, Amancio felt a mysterious joy entering the depths of his being. Evelina had stood up and had walked over to him, stroking his gray hair while at the same time putting her right hand over his chest, as if caressing his heart.

22
Bases for a New Future

The next day, they had a conference with Ribas.

Ernesto and Evelina gave him a succinct report on their visit the day before as he listened attentively.

Not wanting to waste any time, the wise instructor took some folders from a nearby cabinet and began the most important part of the interview, analyzing Tulio Mancini's situation. He believed that the young man had, in fact, displayed very little progress; however, this did not invalidate Mrs. Serpa's commitment; she should continue to help while his rebirth was being organized.

Establishing bases for the future, Ribas had drawn up an immediate and clearly defined action plan for Ernesto and Evelina, in which they should apply their best efforts. Evelina alone would stay at Mancini's side, continuing as much as possible to supervise his mental renewal, whereas Ernesto would travel daily to the physical realm in order to collaborate, within the limits of his capabilities, on behalf of Desiderio and Elisa, who were in need of urgent, fraternal help.

Ribas had contacted several service directors in the Higher Realms, and had been given enough authority to work on solving problems involving the reincarnations that would be needed to re-harmonize the whole group.

But when Evelina heard his instructions, she said sadly:

"So I won't have permission to visit my father for the time being? You know how much I miss him."

"Yes I do, but Desiderio's present situation doesn't warrant being hasty. In order to help him safely, we must examine beforehand every step we take."

"Even mine?"

"Yes, even your actions as his daughter must be taken into account. That rebellious yet noble soul who served as your father possesses admirable qualities that will surface at the right time. We mustn't waste this opportunity. Be patient."

"What do you mean?"

"He should meet you again in a moment of better understanding. Fantini will assist him every day with edifying words, a task similar to the one you will perform with Mancini as you endeavor to awaken him to the joys of Higher Spirituality. This is how both of you will learn to find your mutual affection and respect again."

And after a friendly smile:

"Isn't that what has been happening between you and Tulio?"

Evelina understood and agreed.

"However," the mentor continued, "this won't keep you from intervening in events when circumstances demand it. You can and should see your father again. But we think that your final influence as his daughter must be used on his behalf."

Evelina fell silent, but Fantini cut in:

"Instructor, if I may, I'd like to know if your trustful messenger inspected the situation of our friends in Guaruja."

"Yes, but they weren't there. They're in Sao Paulo."

"At the Vila Mariana house?"

"Caio and Vera were ..."

"And Elisa?

"Exactly six days ago she was admitted for treatment at a mental health clinic."

"My God! How things change!"

"Influenced by Caio Serpa, Vera assumed responsibility and Elisa couldn't oppose it. However, the latest news points out how serious Elisa's prognosis is. I must tell you that the patient has gotten much worse regarding the obsession inflicted on her. Due to the precarious condition of her circulatory system, she was struck by a progressive cerebral thrombosis, which means that death is near. All of this happened immediately after a terrible shock..."

"What shock?" interrupted Fantini astonished.

Unperturbed, the Instructor replied:

"We found out that over the past few weeks Serpa had been pressing Vera to take away her mother's rights to manage her own affairs. He is a lawyer with many connections and he used his influence. He convinced his future mother-in-law to go to the hospital for treatment, assuring her it would be no more than two or three days. But as soon as she went in, he obtained the appropriate documentation to further his purposes and presented them to the pertinent authorities as coming from the young woman he proposed to marry. Of course, the shock to Elisa was exceedingly painful at finding out at the hospital that she no could longer manage her financial resources; such was the case because, despite her obsession, she is perfectly lucid. To us, she is an individual experiencing a tormented mediumship involving psychic phenomena still not understood by those around her ... To Serpa and Vera it's a case of early senility."

"So, now Caio..."

Ernesto's wavering words stuck in his throat.

Ribas concluded:

"Now, Caio is acting as trustee for the patient and her daughter, with legal powers to manage all their assets."

Evelina and Ernesto were stunned.

"In light of the facts, and realizing that we must be as understanding as possible, I must advise you, Fantini, that your plots in Santos were sold the day before yesterday, according to Serpa's instructions, and that he made a profit of a few million cruzeiros[20] as the broker. I don't say this in judgment of the unfortunate behavior of someone else, but because we must plan the future with the duty to look at all the details, even the most undesirable."

"What a shyster!" accused Ernesto. "Good God! Caio acting once more like a criminal?"

Looking at him with paternal benevolence, Ribas warned him:

"Let's avoid being cruel, and let's avoid from any type of vehemence. It's essential that we envelop Serpa and Vera in waves of our deepest sympathy."

"Why?" shouted Fantini, disconsolate.

"You mustn't forget that the two of them are providential in this family group. If you provide Caio with the loving support he needs, he will marry Vera and will be Mancini's father in his new incarnation. Of course, if he collaborates, he will be redeeming his debt: because he took Tulio's life, he must restore it according to the principles of cause and effect. In addition,

---

[20] The Brazilian currency at the time. – Tr.

however, he will bring peace to Evelina by taking responsibility for reeducating a spirit whose emotional misbehavior has caused her so many problems."

"I can understand all that, but..." Ernesto was about to present an unfavorable argument, but Ribas cut him short:

"I know what you're thinking, Fantini. Still so very attached to the family the Lord lent you on earth, you realize that Serpa has begun to take possession of what used to be your considerable fortune. Don't have any illusions. Just as he sold your plots in Santos, he will probably dispose of everything else that you still consider yours, such as your rentals in Sao Paulo, your house in Guaruja, your stocks and bonds, your jewelry, your bank accounts and even your property in Vila Mariana ... Face the facts, my friend. At your discarnation, all your property in the physical realm passed to the domain and control of other hands. Life asks back what it has lent us, giving us in return, wherever it may be, what we made of it in the company of others ... All the transactions we mentioned will certainly occur as soon as Caio makes your daughter his legal wife. Meanwhile, let's refrain from calling him a criminal and a thief. He is, just as we are, a child of God borrowing against the future. Today he is borrowing the assets you left your wife and daughter, the fruit of a very industrious life. He thinks he is being very smart and clever ... but the only person he's fooling is himself."

"How so?"

Their mentor explained calmly:

"Believing he is taking control over large assets, Caio is actually only assuming a larger debt before the Divine Laws. By taking possession of Elisa and Vera's material resources, Caio will instinctively experience the hunger to become richer and richer. He will fall in love with money and soon will feel satiated. Instead of taking advantage of the joys of a simple life, he will be far from true happiness, enslaved for a long time to his ambition of gaining and gaining, accumulating and accumulating ... and in the end all this will revert to benefit ... do you know who?"

"I would love to know," said a discouraged Ernesto.

"Your family, my friend; especially Elisa, whom Caio is presently pushing toward premature discarnation with his insensitive actions in his eagerness to control her financial assets under an illusory scheme of impunity."

"Please explain!" asked Ernesto anxiously.

Ribas took out a small chart from a pile of sheets he had been examining, and pointing out some annotations here and there, he began explaining.

"Elisa's discarnation is predicted within a few days, but after she safely recovers in our colony, her rebirth can occur in five or six years, according to our plan. With the permission of our Superiors, she will be Serpa and Vera's daughter – if you two work at helping them with a lot of love ... She will come after Mancini, their firstborn. It is clear that in around thirty years, the time considered likely for Caio's return to the spirit world, he will give back to his former mother-in-law – now his daughter – as well as to his widow Vera Celina, the entire patrimony that he is taking possession of presently. He will return it greatly increased, while at the same time having worked hard to provide Tulio an enviable material situation in his new existence."

Leaving Evelina and Ernesto astonished at the justice of God's Laws, Ribas ended the meeting by advising them:

"Far be it from us to label Caio as a thief or a delinquent; he is our ally, our friend. What we need to do right now is to ask the Lord to strengthen him with the blessing of physical health and spiritual well-being so that he can live peacefully on the earth for many, many years."

And smiling:

"The time will come when the two of you will do your best to look after him and enable him to increase his honest profits so as to protect the future of your loved ones. Let's beseech God to make Serpa a benevolent, diligent and industrious wealthy man. We need him, and consequently, he needs us."

Realizing that the conversation was coming to an end, Mrs. Serpa hurried to ask:

"Instructor, what about my father? I've been dreaming of his return to a physical body."

"That too has been included in our plans. We knew that, as a dedicated and loving daughter, you would think of helping him ... We've been informed that yesterday you planted in Brigida's maternal heart the seed that will grow with Divine Support, asking her to welcome him into her home as an adopted son. Your appeal was very fortunate, and with such a measure, Amancio Terra, your stepfather, will receive the help he deserves. He killed the body of Desiderio, your father, crazed with the passion that blinded his reason, and then he took over his house and resources. He is a materialist and obviously a criminal, but he is also deeply humane and charitable. He took possession of your father's assets; however, by increasing them through wise and profitable administration, he has become the financial mainstay for more than two hundred reincarnate spirits who work as his servants and tenant farmers, together with their descendants ... For more than 20 years he has watched over them with the protection of an attentive, kind father. He has never abandoned those who got sick, has never despised those who failed, and has never left any children unprotected ... Yes! ... He did kill your father, Desiderio, and he shall answer for that wrong in the courts of life; but he dedicated himself to Brigida, your mother, whose smallest whims he tries to satisfy as a faithful, honest husband ... So many prayers on his behalf have ascended to the Infinite Mercy of God due to the consolation and joy he has spread that he has earned more attention from our Superiors ... Yesterday, we received orders that your plea as a daughter be granted at the right time ... As for your father, according to the petition, he will return with the Lord's Blessing to live with the man he still hates, but he will learn to discover Amancio's noble qualities and will love him dearly as a true father, from whom he will receive self-sacrifice and tenderness, support and a good example."

Ribas didn't say anything for a few moments, and then, as if responding to further questions from his listeners, he added:

"It's true that Amancio has only ten more years left in his physical body, according to the information sent to us for our study purposes; nevertheless, for a man with the amount of service he has rendered, it won't be hard to obtain from our Superiors a moratorium of fifteen to twenty more years, prolonging the time of his current existence ... Considering all this, we hope that he really can win from the Lord the fortune of receiving Desiderio as his son through the collaboration of a humble couple in order to confer on him a new life, and in the future return to him all the assets that he took from him in the past ... You may rest assured, Evelina, that guided by his former tormentor, who has become a worker of the good in the school of labor, your father will be a balanced man with all the resources he needs to be happy."

Ribas paused again for a few seconds and then stated:

"Our plan includes one very important detail ... In the days to come we will be called to bring Serpa and Amancio's homes closer together, because, reincarnated, Desiderio and Elisa will enjoy a happy marriage in the fullness of their youth ... We will do our best to bring Desiderio here shortly to say goodbye before he leaves for the physical world."

Evelina wept with joy as she pondered God's perfect justice, while Ernesto reflected with amazement on the logic of the plan.

Containing her tear-filled emotions, Evelina asked:

"And my mother?"

"Your dear mother," Ribas explained, "will accompany Amancio's destiny ...Your father married her but he didn't love her ... such that, according to our records, you were still in the cradle when he was already looking for other love interests."

"So many plans!" Fantini speculated, "To transform words into deeds demands a lot of work! Who'll be responsible for carrying out so many plans?"

The mentor looked at them benevolently and answered:

"Haven't you ever heard about spirit guides?"

Ernesto and Evelina both looked surprised.

Ribas made it clearer:

"That's right ... The two of you will be in charge of the upcoming endeavor, with all the associated tasks the job implies. You will work hard to ensure that Serpa and Vera get married; that Elisa recovers as quickly as possible after her discarnation; that Desiderio returns to physical rebirth under the appropriate conditions. Also, you will help Elisa return to the earth and will be in charge of watching over her during infancy and childhood. Moreover, you will be collaborating not only to help Desiderio's future mother obtain the appropriate conditions to receive him into the womb, but also to make Desiderio feel adequately settled in his position as an adopted child ... And we cannot forget our Mancini, who will continue to demand special attention. You will have to look after his progress in the future, and the marriage of Elisa and Desiderio later on, after we have taken measures to bring the Serpa and Terra families together."

And filled with good humor, Ribas concluded:

"You have thirty years of work ahead of you, my friends! To start things off, consider yourselves connected to our colony for at least that long!"

Ernesto looked at Evelina with enormous tenderness. And he had thought that she and he had been expelled from the memories of those they loved most – almost completely forgotten, rejected and replaced. The ex-Mrs. Serpa – because the young woman honestly believed herself free from Caio as far as any commitment of an affective nature – returned Ernesto's look and attuned herself to his ideas and emotions. They were together in the undertaking that had been imparted to them; their consciences were at peace. Fantini seemed more spiritualized due to the suffering of the last few days, as if the fire of hidden afflictions had remolded the shape and outline of his face. Looking at each other, they understood without words. None of their loved ones on earth – except for Brigida, who still had thoughts of tenderness and longing for her departed daughter – had any thoughts for them. Nonetheless, they needed to act and labor on their behalf. And so, like allies who meet again to carry out venerable tasks in the field of life, they silently promised each other to join hearts, transferring to each other the loving heritage they had brought back from earth, convinced that they needed mutual support for the long journey that was just starting in their longing for redemption.

23
Ernesto at Work

Fantini and Evelina's work of spiritual assistance was going very well, shifting between Tulio's progress and their attempts to re-approach Desiderio, who wouldn't let go of Elisa, who was now on her own in the sanatorium.

Ernesto's work was becoming increasingly difficult, as his enemy wasted no opportunity to attack him with accusations and insults. On the other hand, Elisa's physical health was worsening by the day, and his efforts to reach her were nearly fruitless. Concerned about this situation, he went to Ribas to explain his worries. He wanted to know why a suffering spirit, so encased in ideas of revenge, had acquired such powers of judgment, to the point of pointing out the smallest flaws in Ernesto's character.

"Ah! My friend! My friend!" confessed the instructor. "Our brothers and sisters shackled to despair and rebelliousness can find many reasons to criticize us when we perform our roles in title only."

"What do you mean?"

"Very often, while in the world, we are title-holders of this or that set of responsibilities, but we fail to execute them effectively. We wear the labels of husbands, parents, children or administrators, but we don't really tend to the obligations they entail. I'm sure you can understand that. I myself had the title of husband; that is, I got married and embraced the commitment to a family, but I believed my responsibilities were limited to being the head of the household and paying the bills at the end of the month. In reality, I never shared my wife's concerns about our children's emotional upbringing, and from what I can remember, I never sat down with any of them to hear about their problems and dreams, although I demanded them to carry my name with honor."

Grasping this subtle admonition, Fantini once more had to come to grips with his own conscience.

He came to the honest conclusion that he hadn't been the husband or father he should have been. It was only there in that spirit colony after the death of his physical body that, through the difficult struggles of self-correction, he had finally understood that money does not do the work of the heart. Disheartened and saddened, Ernesto refrained from discussing the matter any further. His smiling mentor, however, comforted him as they parted:

"Don't be discouraged! ... Let's listen to our opponents' criticisms and accept them with humility when they are true and useful. Let's use this key, Fantini: humility ... It will work effectively in the solution of our biggest problems. Let's be true Christians – loving, serving and forgiving."

Attentive to his friend's constant instructions, Fantini dedicated himself more and more to the duties of true fraternity, whether tolerating the attacks of his suffering-debilitated wife, or bearing with heroic resignation the insults of the unfortunate Desiderio, who was always ready to hurl all types of verbal abuse at him.

After twenty-six days of dedication to his work, Fantini was surprised to see Serpa visit his future mother-in-law for the first time.

Very well dressed, the lawyer sat down with the patient in a private room with the permission of the institution's administration, having told them that he wanted to verify the patient's condition for himself in order to provide accurate information to his fiancée.

With them there were the two discarnate men, Desiderio and Fantini, both anxious to see what would come from the interview.

Once they were alone, Elisa, with the serene words of a mother, expressed her desire to see her daughter in order to show her she was mentally sound, and for her to sponsor her return home. Both Fantini and Desiderio were touched by the humble attitude in which the pleas poured from the woman defeated by the circumstances.

Serpa wouldn't budge.

"Absolutely not! You will not be released as you wish; your prognosis is not good."

"Why not?"

"The information regarding your behavior prevents us from letting you return."

"Behavior? What behavior?"

"You cry constantly for no reason; you talk to yourself; you talk to shadows."

"I'm simply misunderstood. I see what I see."

"Vera calls here every day and the nurses all confirm that your mental problems haven't diminished."

"Caio," admonished Elisa showing her uneasiness, "in spite of all that, I'm begging you as a gentleman to bring Vera to see me!"

"What for? To traumatize her with your fantasies? Don't you think your daughter has already suffered enough with your crying and sleepless nights?"

"Oh, Caio!"

"You know I'm about to be your son-in-law; I have the right to get involved."

"I don't know anyone who has the right to come between a mother and her children," asserted the patient, now enunciating each word with a tone of deep sorrow. "I haven't complained about your meddling in the affairs of my house to the point that I can't even write a simple check."

"Don't whine about it," blurted Caio aggressively. "I became your trustee because your daughter wanted me to. I have enough work already and I wouldn't have come here on my own to help you."

"I'm not complaining and I'm depending on your honesty to look after my daughter's interests ... As for me..."

"What are you getting at?"

"As for me, the two of you won't have to put up with me much longer. Dust to dust ..."

"Why talk like that? What's so horrible about it? Death is the end for all of us. If you want to make me feel sorry for you, it won't work."

"Oh, for God's sake! I just want to see my daughter!"

"Well, as long as you're not normal and can't meet her without making her feel bad, you won't be seeing her."

"But why won't you let me, when I always received you in my home as if you were my own son?"

"That's a lie! You hate me ... The only reason you didn't throw me out was because Vera didn't let you ... because I'm the man she has chosen to look after her future."

The patient looked painfully astonished as he continued:

"Rest assured that both Vera and I know very well that you have already lived your life; now it's our turn ... A sick old mother-in-law isn't going to come between us and our plans."

Sudden repulsion took over Elisa's mind and she reacted with a frenetic scream:

"You bastard!"

Upon Elisa's indignation, Desiderio – the discarnate spirit who in fact controlled all her faculties – took command of her mind and the crisis progressed, overbearing and terrible.

Possessed, Elisa attacked the visitor with the intention of strangling him in a fit of uncharacteristic swearing.

Serpa retreated in unconcealed surprise, making room for a nurse who restrained the widow, while at the same time Ernesto, on an impulse, put a stop to the obsessor's unruly behavior.

Order was re-established.

The nurse on duty was helped by two others to take Elisa back to her room, and then she came back to apologize.

"Don't worry, sir. It was a crisis like so many others she's had ... She'll get over it."

"I understand," replied Caio politely. "Dona Elisa has always treated me like she was my mother. Poor woman! Her nerves are really shot."

While the two were talking, Fantini fraternally held Desiderio back with the help of other discarnates working in the sanatorium.

One of them suggested the agitated aggressor be confined, while others stated that ever since Elisa had arrived, Desiderio had been a helpful and quiet companion for the patient, who found in him both a support and a friend.

Upon hearing allusions to possible confinement, Evelina' father saw that he could face the possibility of losing his beloved Elisa, so he settled down.

With the intent of reassuring the discarnate guards, Ernesto took advantage of the opportunity and introduced Desiderio as his dear brother, pointing out that he had lost control due to certain family difficulties; that he, Fantini, was there for the sole purpose of helping him get rid of any destructive memories.

The guards left.

Ernesto invited his rival to follow him. Desiderio acquiesced, and the two of them sat on a large bench in the nearby garden.

Desiderio was weeping in anger, barred as he had been from beating the lawyer as he had wished.

"Did you see how vile he is?" he exploded, looking at Fantini with less hate. "I don't know why I haven't put an end to that bastard! ... First, he murders a colleague, that lawyer Tulio Mancini; then he kills my daughter bit by bit; now he wants to destroy Elisa after shamelessly stealing her money."

Ernesto looked at him kindly and said:

"Desiderio, forgive us for all the evil we've done to you and listen to me! Calm down, for God's sake! I'm not asking you this for us, but for Elisa, whom you love so dearly ... Right now, the only thing I want is peace between us. Compose yourself so we can face reality; I can tell you that our patient is at the end of her physical endurance."

"I'm somewhat aware of that fact," replied Desiderio a little less hostile, displaying his willingness for agreement and understanding for the first time, "but I'll fight like a bull to defend her. I'll give her my strength, my life! My soul is hers, just as the body in which she breathes is my body ... We live in the same cell of flesh; we think with the same mind!"

"Thank God," Fantini agreed humbly, "that I've come to understand that this is how it is and how it should be."

And revealing the high degree of selflessness he was in the process of acquiring, Fantini continued:

"When you spoke to me with fraternal sincerity on the first day we met again, I saw that Elisa had found in you the support she needed, and believe me, the only thing I want now is to see her happy with you ... I know for a fact that our patient won't be in her physical body much longer, and today's shock will certainly take its toll."

"Ah! That despicable Caio!"

"No, Desiderio! Don't be like that ... I beg you to be patient and tolerant ... Shouldn't we be tired of rebelliousness and hatred? For my crime of trying to kill you, I spent my earthly existence in bitter remorse, constantly trying to run from myself and wasting the best years of life in the world of men ... And you, my friend, for not having forgiven me or our friend Amancio, you have been living in the cruel world of tribulations reserved for impenitent and suffering spirits ... Why couldn't Elisa's flood of tears spell the end of our foolishness? A sacred truce? Soon she'll be delivered from physical pain, but what about us, my friend? What will become of us if, having abandoned the body of heavy matter, we continue as spirits tormented by thoughts of guilt and condemnation, crime and punishment? She will depart ..."

Desiderio, however, was angered by these statements announcing the separation and shouted impulsively:

"Elisa will not leave my arms; she will not abandon me! ... I will not leave her!"

"Desiderio, all our protests against the forces of life are useless. God's laws will prevail. Elisa draws support from you, but she also loves her daughter, and knowing that she is being kept from her tenderness, she unconsciously longs to die, a wish that will occur more quickly since she has become certain of Serpa's unfortunate conduct ... The poor woman will of course dwell on the thought of discarnation, believing it to be a direct means to your company; however, the unforeseen will happen ... Death will place her directly opposite to you ... She doesn't have your mental structure or your willingness to remain around here ... Certainly, today she resents her son-in-law, but tomorrow she will be able to absolve him and vouch for him before the Messengers of the Higher Life through her prayers ... Despite her irascible temperament, she doesn't hate anybody and has never shown any inclination for revenge."

Desiderio sat on the ground with his head in his hands, and wept in greater despair.

"Forgive, my friend! ... Forgive all of us in your compassion, including Caio!"

"Never! Never!"

"I'm the one who acknowledges the injustices we perpetrated against you; I'm the one who can see the nobility of your heart ... Forgive me and listen ... I'm grateful for your dedication to the woman I failed to make happy, and your tenderness for the daughter to whom you became a selfless protector ... For all you've done, I ask you further to extend to us, your executioners, the vibrations of your compassion and sympathy."

"Ah! Fantini! Fantini!" roared Desiderio as if struggling with himself not to surrender to his emotions. "Why do you tempt me with an impossible reconciliation? Why are you making such an effort to change me?"

"Desiderio, in the physical world we work in particular with dense matter to transform rock, metal, land and springs ... Here, in the spirit world, we deal especially with the powers of the spirit to renew souls and consciences, beginning with our own ... Listen to me! ... Remember that Elisa has a lot of friends calling her to the Higher Realms, as was the case with your dear Evelina! ... For the love of Evelina, whom you keep in your memory as a guardian angel, don't you want to sublimate your actions, starting with the forgiveness that we need and implore?"

"Evelina! ... Evelina, my dear daughter!" sighed the unfortunate spirit through a torrent of tears. "No, I won't drag her into this conversation! ... Evelina must be living in the house of the angels! ... May I suffer in hell, comforted by no one but myself; may I wallow in the muck that I deserve; but may happiness bless my daughter in heaven!"

"And what if she herself were to come to you one day to plead our cause, to assist us, to beseech your mercy for us, who owe you so much?"

Desiderio made a great effort to speak, overcoming the barrier of pain oppressing the depths of his soul. However, at this point, a compassionate spirit assistant at the institution approached them to inform them of a sudden occurrence. After her violent crisis, Elisa had fallen into deep prostration due to the rupture of a delicate brain vessel. Her discarnation was only a matter of hours.

The two men forgot everything else in order to help.

Immediately notified by phone, Vera and Serpa, alarmed as to the new direction the situation had taken, set out together for the institution. They found Elisa dying in an atmosphere of peace and care.

In spite of extending words of consolation and hope, the friendly doctor was clear on the prognosis: "There is nothing more to do but wait."

Vera Celina knelt in tears close to her mother, whose mouth would never again bless her through her earthly body.

Caio, obviously upset, watched the scene smoking one cigarette after another.

Nurses were coming and going, eager to be of help, and spirit assistants were forming a magnetic current of support for

Fantini's widow so that her transition from one world to the other would be quicker and less troubling.

Ernesto set off for the spirit world in order to receive instructions from Ribas in light of the emergency, while Desiderio planted himself at Elisa's bedside, immersed in revolt and despair.

For another eight hours Elisa's heart sustained the motionless body.

At daybreak, she opened her eyes wide and tried to gaze into her daughter's for the unutterable goodbye; however, at that moment she saw Serpa next to her bed looking at her, and in spite of being incapable of nourishing any vestiges of hatred in the depths of her soul, she encased her heart in a thick cloud of resentment, and mentally asked Desiderio to protect and defend her. That rash appeal was all it took. Desiderio, avidly seizing the thoughts that would be her last in the corporeal envelope, bound himself to her like someone absorbing all her strength.

Vera sensed that her mother was finally surrendering to the great repose and desperately tried to bring her back to life:

"Mother! Mother! ... Dear mother!"

No response came from the motionless lips.

Elisa Fantini let her head drop onto the pillow as her body stopped moving forever.

In the ward of the sanatorium, the veil of death fell over that existence, fraught with tribulations and problems on the stage of the world. However, backstage in the spirit realm, the drama had not yet finished. Bound to the deceased by the force of her final desire, Desiderio, burning in flames of hatred, held one of Elisa's hands in his own, preventing her from leaving ... Though only half conscious, Elisa perceived that she was tied to him and shackled to her corpse as she

heard her unfortunate companion saying over and over again
that he would never leave her.

***

Brothers and sisters on the earth: in the midst of the
tribulations of human existence, learn to tolerate and to forgive! ...
No matter how hurt or slandered, offended or cursed, forget evil
by doing good! ... You who have had your trust betrayed, or
your spirit torn in the traps of darkness, light the light of love
wherever you are! Friends, you who have been vilified or insulted
in your most sublime intentions, forget these offenses and bless
the tribulations that mold your heart for the Greater World! ...
Sisters, who have suffered indescribable torments in your flesh,
despised by smiling tormentors who left you distraught in
anguish after having lured you with false promises, bless those
who have destroyed your dreams! ... Single mothers, banished
from home and beaten by life, falling into prostitution for
having kept in your womb the children of your disgrace without
resorting to an abortion; suffering mothers who are many times
denied the right to defend yourselves – a right extended even to
criminals in prisons – forgive your tormentors! ... Parents, who
bear on your bruised shoulders the burden of thankless children;
children, who endure in flesh and soul the tyranny and brutality
of insensitive parents; and spouses, pierced with the daggers of
misunderstanding and cruelty within the walls of your home:
acquit each other! ... Sufferers of all kinds of obsessive conditions,
weave veils of compassion and hope over the unfortunate spirits –
incarnate or discarnate – who torment you at every hour! ...
People, harmed or persecuted all over the world, forgive those
who have become instruments of your afflictions and tears! ...
When you feel the temptation to strike back, remember the

One who encouraged us to "love our enemies" and to "pray for those who persecute and slander us!" Remember the Christ of God, who preferred to be condemned rather than to condemn, because those who practice evil know not what they are doing! ... Know for certain that the laws of death do not exempt anyone, and do not forget that on the day of your great farewell to those who stay behind in this place of trials, it is only through the blessings of love and peace of a clear conscience that you will find the deliverance you have longed for!

24
Evelina at Work

Before sunrise, Ernesto, Evelina and some friends from the Institute of Spiritual Watch Care – including Brother Plotino, who, at Instructor Ribas' request, was leading the small aid group – set off for Sao Paulo with the aim of collaborating with the spirit assistants working to free Elisa from the prison of her remains.

After being informed that her daughter Vera had given instructions for the body to be sent home, they set out for Vila Mariana.

Evelina's heart was pounding. She would be seeing her father for the first time. In her memory she cherished the image she had gleaned from family photographs. She was anxious to understand him, to support him.

Ernesto encouraged her.

As they neared their destination, Plotino asked the team to stop. He said that he would go inside first by himself to make a brief inspection to determine what needed to be done.

Elisa's body was being tended to by her daughter, who, in turn, was being comforted by Serpa and some friends from the neighborhood. Elisa's spirit was being tended to by several spirit benefactors; however, she was semi-conscious and remained at an impasse, since, bound to Desiderio by one of his hands and nourished by his energies flooding her soul, she seemed to be enjoying the strange hypnosis.

Plotino, the compassionate discarnate nurse in charge of freeing the widow from her remains through magnetic procedures, shared his concerns: even if he could convince Mrs. Fantini to abandon her now useless physical body, he wouldn't be able to compel her perfectly lucid mind. He might force her to leave the body, but he would not be able to isolate her mentally from her rebellious companion – she had willingly put herself in his hands.

It was crucial that someone with sufficient power of persuasion convince Desiderio to change his attitude.

Brother Plotino approached Desiderio with fraternal kindness and asked for his help so that Elisa could be freed and taken to a shelter for recovery.

Desiderio got even closer than he had been to her and roared in a wild voice:

"Clowns! ... You'll not take me from here! What do you want? She's my woman ... No one will dissuade me with their prayers and litanies. I know what I'm talking about! I know all about those who cannot be kept from each other in the awful caves where we dwell ... No one, but no one, will remove me from this room!"

"Someone will, Desiderio," stated Plotino serenely.

"Who? Tell me who!"

The envoy smiled patiently and whispered only:

"God."

The rebellious spirit shouted a terrible blasphemy and Plotino rejoined his companions. He explained what had happened and what their next steps should be. Now was the time for Evelina's personal intervention. The rest of the group would pray in order to assist her while she went inside alone to try to get her father to change his mind; surely, Desiderio would not hesitate to obey her.

The power of thoughts focused on one sole objective would soon be seen.

With no desire for spectacles, but united in one profound and sincere purpose of projecting the energies of love into the work at hand, those hearts in prayer cast a broad layer of sapphire-blue light over the front door, investing Evelina for the blessed mission delegated to her. Spiritually connected to the friends who had become her base of balance and support, Evelina entered the room as if she were a star suddenly transfigured into a woman.

Terrified, Desiderio stared at the apparition and fell on his knees! Yes! It was her! he thought: his daughter, his beloved daughter whom he had never forgotten, even while he had been immersed in the thickest darkness!

As Evelina fixed her gaze on her wretched father in a display of radiant and kind tenderness, he saw himself in the soft light she was emitting ... He saw himself in the misery of a prisoner who had remained for years and years at the bottom of a cell without the least regard for himself. He thought of himself as a monster in front of an angel, and like a beaten, wounded dog, he intended to crawl away and escape.

The young woman read his mind and said simply:
"Father!"

Desiderio felt that voice piercing his innards ... Yes, that word had come from that dearest of souls, whom he had believed would never come down from heaven to speak to him ... Shaking, he kneeled again, the utter bewilderment finally overcoming him in an explosion of tears.

"So, it is really you, dear child? It really is you whom God has sent to ask the impossible of me?"

Evelina approached him, put her right hand on his tormented head, and the dialogue continued:

"My dear father, of course God is blessing our meeting again, but in fact, the two of us are the agents not of the impossible, but of our reunion in his name, in the name of our Creator and Father of mercy."

"What do you want from me?!"

"I have come to invite you to be with me ... Do you think that all this time has gone by without my having dreamed of this moment? I went through childhood and adolescence cherishing your photographs; I got married praying for your blessings; and when the Divine Plan took me from my physical body, I envisioned the ideal of meeting you again!"

The wretch made a gesture of self-pity and moaned:

"See what they have done to me, those criminals who destroyed us..."

"Oh, Father, you mustn't blame anyone! ... You must have suffered, but pain is always blessed in God's sight. You must have endured difficult trials, but we now know that every day is an opportunity for renewal and higher destinations!"

"Surely, they must have told you in the Divine Realms that I didn't die because of an accident."

"Yes, I now know the whole truth about us."

"So, you can see that my tormentors are yours too, that we were both robbed by the same crooks! ... If in heaven there is no memory of evil, let me remind you that Amancio Terra, the monster who took the role of your stepfather..."

Because his weeping was forcing him to make long pauses, Evelina explained humbly:

"Would you be angry with me if I told you that he wanted what was best for me and that he always respected me as if I were his own daughter? ... While we cannot deny that he committed a grave wrong against you before the Divine Laws, I believe that the repentance he has been carrying inside for more than twenty years speaks of the regeneration that has turned him into a good man."

"Don't forget that he banished you from home when you were still a young child."

"He sent me to school, Father. He gave me the discipline that delivered me from the temptations to which I would otherwise have succumbed during my time on earth. He never refused to help me and never objected to my desire to get married. During my childhood, he encouraged me to study; he showed interest in my grades and praised my goodwill with the love and gifts that only you could have given me ... It's true that my stepfather never replaced you in my heart, but your daughter cannot be ungrateful toward someone who gave her so much! ... At home he was always the guardian of our happiness ... I never saw him do the least thing to displease my mother."

"Ah! Don't speak of Brigida, that shameful woman!"

"Oh! Dearest father! Why condemn the one who brought us together? What could my still-young mother have done to raise me without the support of a companion? By accepting Amancio's help she wasn't deliberately marrying the unfortunate hunter who caused your discarnation, but rather the friend that you yourself brought home one day, according to Mom's recollections in her moments of longing and discouragement ... I want you to know that she always taught me to revere your memory and to honor your name."

In light of his daughter's superior understanding, Desiderio wept even harder in a show of self-pity, giving the impression of someone searching for any reason he could find to be miserable.

"Maybe you're unaware of the fact that I'm linked to the family of another enemy whom I cannot forgive: Ernesto Fantini, the traitor who tried to kill me, providing your stepfather with the ideal situation to take my life! ... This woman, dead to others but alive in my hands: she was his wife ... Blinded by jealousy, Fantini meant to kill me, but instead he only succeeded in bringing me closer to her, whereas Brigida's behavior kept me away from my own home. Think about your father's dreadful fate! ... Expelled from my home after the death of my body, because my persecutor had taken over, I had to seek shelter in the house of another, where, in the memories of Elisa – now dead to the world – I found my sustenance!"

"Who can know God's designs, Father? Aren't we all experiencing our testimonies of love in light of the wrongs and commitments of past lives? I ask Divine Providence to bless our sister Elisa and to reward her for all the good she has done for us. As for Ernesto Fantini, you should know that he has been my dedicated friend in the spirit world ... Long before he knew my connection to your heart, he cared for me, restoring my energies. At every step on this new pathway he has been a support, a true brother."

"Evelina, my dear daughter, you must have acquired the goodness of angels to see these criminals as benefactors, but I cannot see human creatures through heavenly eyes. I'm a man, simply an unfortunate man ... In spite of everything, I cannot believe you can hold such regard for the man who was your tormentor in your own home, that criminal evading prison, masquerading right here in front of us ... Caio Serpa..."

"What are you saying, Father?"

And Evelina spoke even more compassionately:

"Caio was my generous guide; he helped me understand life more surely ... In my youth he provided me with dreams of happiness that helped me live ... With him, I imagined heaven on earth ... and if as a husband he expected from me the happiness I couldn't give him, is that any reason for us to condemn him? Obviously, he incurred a debt with Mancini, a debt he will most surely pay at the right time. But why despise those who have been the object of our love when we realize they are not as happy as we thought? Don't you think that our delinquent brothers and sisters are ill and in need of attention? Why not show compassion for the victims of insanity as we do with the casualties of disasters that rob their lives? Are the maimed in spirit any different from the maimed in body?"

Her rebellious father's weeping became more forlorn:

"Poor me! I don't know how to forgive! ... The weight of life is crushing me like useless rubbish."

"Father, hasn't it ever occurred to you that we are all God's children and that we depend on each other?"

"I can't! ... I can't understand why I should embrace those who have harmed me."

"Don't you want to move on? To be free and happy?"

"Oh, yes!"

"Then forget all evil. Haven't you ever thought about the power of time? Time helps us find the fountain of love that washes away all our sins."

"Time, my dear Evelina? To spirits like me, the clock is a device that drives us insane ... the day before yesterday, yesterday and today I have suffered because I loathe the three wolves: Amancio, Ernesto, and Caio, and I suffer in order to defend three lambs from them: Elisa, you and Vera, since long ago I pushed Brigida away from me! ... You surely know that Vera is under the spell of that rascal who used to be your husband!"

"Have compassion, dear father! ... Let's think of Vera and Caio with the best sentiments possible! ... Let's think of the future ... Tomorrow they will be our invaluable friends and dedicated care takers!"

"You see only what is good, but I see the evil that defeats the good."

"That's not the way it is. You think you are perfectly whole in spirit, when, in fact, as is still the case with me, you need assistance and readjustment. At first, I too felt that life had treated me unfairly! ... On many occasions, I thought of my mother and stepfather as my enemies who wanted me out of the house so that I wouldn't come between them and their happiness. But in the institute to where I was taken by God's mercy, I began to consider them as our true friends, from whom I received all the support I could assimilate ... After seeing Caio so deeply attached to Vera Celina, I wallowed in profound anguish until a few days ago, believing my earthly husband to be a very ungrateful man. At the same time, I criticized Celina as an intruder and a thief of the love I had on the earth. However, God's infinite mercy came upon the dryness of my small-minded sentiments through lessons given by selfless instructors – doctors and nurses of the Divine Compassion. I recovered my balance and concluded that Caio and Vera are our true brother and sister ... They are what they are, just as we are what we are, and God expects us to love each other the way he allows us to be! ... It's indispensable, dear father, that we understand and help each other and that we move on! We must press on, redeeming the debts of yesterday so that our tomorrow can be better ... The Almighty has planted flowers and blessings all along the pathway ... Understanding this makes us look for the path, and helping others will keep us on course! Love never fails and God has created us for boundless love!"

Desiderio wept, unable to say a word.

Evelina continued:

"Reason it out for yourself. Naturally, despite the inner conflicts that detached him spiritually from home, our brother Ernesto feels for Elisa an affection originating from his good sentiments, something that compels him, with all his heart and according to the discernment he now has, to see in you the companion you have been and will be for her before God. So, why shouldn't we likewise grant Caio the right to give himself to Vera, to enjoy the happiness that I could not give him, not even when I was in the physical world?"

"Ah, my dear daughter!" exclaimed her alarmed father, "doesn't such selflessness mean moral suicide?"

"No, dear father. True love is higher than that ... I now understand that distorted affections can be corrected in the holy institute of the family through reincarnation ... God allows us to embrace as children the same individuals we were not able to love under different sentimental circumstances! Our thoughts of tenderness for each other will one day be free and pure, like two crystalline springs that run together on the stony ground of the planet, or like the light of the stars that interlaces without depriving them of their grandeur and originality on the immense highways of the heavens."

After a long pause, accompanied by the respectful silence of the discarnate friends who were with them, Evelina continued:

"If clouds of anguish are still dwelling in your soul, drive them away and let's press onward, wishing for peace! ... For now, let our Elisa distance herself from any unpleasant memories! Set her free and you will see that the woman you chose will belong to you more strongly! ... Help her to ascend new pathways and she will come back to you! ... Don't lock up in the dungeon of rotting flesh the one who deserves your most sacred dedication!

Elisa will be thankful to you, and on our part, we solemnly promise you before the Infinite Mercy of God that you will see her again in the colony that is presently our home, where both of you will prepare yourselves with our love for a new life together, together once more and happier! ... Accept my plea, dear father!"

"No, no!" roared Desiderio in a more violent fit of despair. "I'm a sinner; I cannot pretend!"

At this time, the highest, most touching moment of the reunion took place.

With her hands on her father's head, Evelina raised her eyes to heaven and pleaded:

"O God of all Goodness! ... My father and I are the two remaining members of a large spiritual family that is scattered for now! ... Grant us, O most merciful God, if it is your will, perseverance in harmony under the same yearning for redemption!"

Her voice, however, stuck in her throat, suffocated with grief, and as she bent toward her father's brow, the tears that were streaming down her face like a divine balm reached the unhappy Desiderio, transfiguring his soul.

Touched by concealed energies, Desiderio let out a painful groan, and immediately released the dead woman's hand. Embracing his daughter's feet, he cried out fervently:

"Ah! Evelina, Evelina! ... My child, my child! Take me wherever you wish! ... I trust you! ... Appease the fire in my spirit that has known only hate! ... Help me, God! ... Help me, God!"

Aided by the strength of her praying companions, Evelina lifted him with ease as if holding a frightened child close to her heart.

Discarnate nurses hurried to remove Elisa from her lifeless body like a group of technicians working quickly to remove a worn-out garment, while Brother Plotino and his coworkers placed the semi-conscious Desiderio in the ambulance that would take him to his new spiritual home.

***

Someone had discreetly followed the entire dialogue. It was Instructor Ribas, who had come unannounced to the Vila Mariana house in order to encourage through prayer the ward of the Institute of Spiritual Watch Care in her unforgettable witness. The moment he saw her helping her father toward a sublime metamorphosis, the venerable guide, perhaps remembering episodes of his own life, withdrew in silence with tear-filled eyes.

As for us, back on the street, we limited ourselves to gazing up at the firmament, where the purplish dawn announced the eternal renewal, suggesting that we praise God's unlimited mercy ... and thus we prayed, without being able to articulate one single word.

25
A New Direction

After checking Desiderio and Elisa into a hospital with the help of kind assistants, Ernesto and Evelina returned on the afternoon of that same day to Sao Paulo, eager to check on Vera's reaction to the new situation. Informed as to the future, when Vera's participation and collaboration would be of the utmost importance for their peace of mind, Ernesto and Evelina understood that their role was to support her with even more warmth and tenderness.

Desiderio's surrender to the renewing ideals they both shared was another crucial point in their work plan, and they hoped to readjust Caio's attitudes in order to provide them with a more propitious area of action.

They found Vera Celina weeping with grief, supported by friends and family.

A taciturn Caio had taken over, giving orders in the household.

Once the funeral procession got underway, the two discarnate visitors, as well as many other friends from the higher spheres of spirituality, settled into the family car next to Vera. When they arrived at the cemetery, Ernesto supported his daughter, while Evelina accompanied her ex-husband, who seemed to have fixed his attention on another grave near the one where Fantini's widow's remains would be buried.

Serpa did this deliberately. He didn't want to watch the burial.

Fully perceiving the influence of the wife he had buried a little more than two years ago, he remembered Evelina, and without meaning to, he saw her image on the screen of his memory.

Not far from him, Vera was weeping in the arms of her friends, while he was gloomily ruminating, ruminating ...

He remembered when he had left his wife in another cemetery, the Quarta Parada[21]. He recalled her departure, the details of what had happened ...

That too had been at sunset, just like today in Vila Mariana. And the same unanswered questions came to his mind.

Did life really end under piles of stone and ash? Where did the dead go in the event that there actually was life after death? Where were the parents he had lost in his youth? Where was Evelina, the wife he had loved so much in the early days of his youth, and whom illness and death had taken from him? As he remembered her, he felt connected to another painful memory: Tulio Mancini ... His heart felt constricted and he asked himself how he could have given in to the madness of murdering his colleague ... The crime surfaced in his memory in all its details.

Serpa tried to rid himself of these thoughts as they came to mind, but he felt incomprehensively hooked to the past.

---

[21] A cemetery in Sao Paulo. – Auth.

He couldn't perceive Evelina right there next to him as she guided him to wake up to the truth.

"Caio, what are you doing with your life?" she asked gently.

The attorney didn't register the question with his physical eardrums, but he did hear her in the acoustics of his soul. He thought he was talking to himself: "Caio, what are you doing with your life?" He unconsciously repeated his discarnate companion's words in the secret chamber of his consciousness and realized that time was flying by without him taking stock of himself ... How had he been using the treasure of time? What uses had he made of his health and money? What blessings had he spread by means of his academic degree? As a friend, he had murdered a colleague; as a husband, he hadn't even had the courage to be good to his wife stricken by illness!"

His eyes stumbled involuntarily upon Elisa's funeral ritual and he asked himself what he might have meant to the dead woman ... Quite frankly, he didn't feel good about himself as he recalled how impatiently and harshly he had always treated her, concerned as he was in taking her daughter's love away from her.

Acknowledging the appalling judgment of his own conscience, he gazed at Vera, albeit at quite a distance, in order to discern her inner thoughts by the look on her face.

"Caio," whispered Evelina into the ears of his soul, "think about your responsibilities ... It's time for you to legalize your situation with the young woman who has wholly entrusted herself to you."

Still convinced he was talking to himself, Serpa silently reproduced Evelina's comment in his mind, unaware that his discarnate wife was perceiving his answers. Believing it to be only self-talk, he continued the inner monologue: Legalize my situation with Vera? Get married? Why?

Yes, he argued, he had promised to marry her, but he wouldn't jump into it without giving it further study. He had already been a man tied to the duties of a husband, and he did not intend to have another relationship full of constraints. Moreover, he considered, he was a man with solid experience in the world. In social circles he had heard many unflattering references to Elisa's daughter, which would not recommend her as a wife. Several young men had denigrated her reputation as a woman. Why should he give his name to such a fickle creature?

"Caio, who are you to judge?"

Evelina's question pierced his soul like a burning thought that both softened and frightened him.

And as if he were thinking aloud, talking mentally to himself, he continued receiving more exhortations, striking his innermost being like arrows of truth.

"Caio, who are you to judge? Aren't you also burdened with dreadful debts before the Law? By what right can you so hastily condemn a young woman deceived by others due to the lack of proper moral support?!"

Based on these arguments, Serpa continued asking himself ... Was it fair to continue taking advantage of her now that she was practically alone in the world? If he left her, where would she go? And who was he, Caio Serpa, if not a man reaching middle age and in need of someone's dedication to prevent the train of his life from derailing? He had experienced the entire range of physical pleasures, but how had he profited from it, if he had turned every expression of love into abuse and irresponsibility? What had he reaped from the noisy night life – so full of voices but empty of meaning – except weariness and disillusionment? As far as he could remember, he had never helped anyone. He knew how to be affable, as long as the circumstances did not inconvenience him. All it took, however, was one little thing to make him feel uncomfortable and he would find this or that escape route, with the clear intent of not wanting to be put out. Hadn't the time come to actually help someone, to do something for someone else for a change? At first, bent on winning her over, he had showered Vera with tenderness and love, captivating her full attention; afterwards, the satiety of those who no longer love after the flame of desire has gone out in their physical appeal. But he could not deny the fact that the young woman had given him her highest expressions of trust. Vera Celina had surrendered to him completely, and in the end she had not hesitated to humiliate her own mother in order to transfer all her assets to him.

Serpa registered all of his discarnate wife's arguments in the fashion of a lamp that thinks itself its own source of light, unaware that it receives it from the power plant.

He tried to counter argue:

"Get married? Tie myself down? Why? Don't I enjoy all the pleasures of a married man without the chains of marriage?"

Evelina's voice once again resounded in his mind:

"Yes, you are the strongest element in this relationship, but how can you protect yourself from temptations in the future; how can you keep yourself from your own philandering tendencies if not by giving her, the gentler element that looks up to you, the necessary peace of mind to enable it to work for you? Do you think you are free of the irresponsible inclination so characteristic of your love life? Wouldn't it be better for you to guarantee her peace of mind and preserve your own by bringing some structure to your life? Think about it! Imagine yourself in front of your own mother, for nearly all men seek in their spouses the maternal support that adulthood stole from their childhood ... Would you respect a man – in this case your own father – who trampled on the deepest yearnings of her heart?

Wouldn't she be more deserving of your support and love if you saw her ill-treated, abandoned and forgotten by the one to whom she so trustingly gave herself? Why do you delve into the past to revile the woman you love, when, in fact, it makes her someone more in need of your understanding and protection?!"

After these admonitions, the former Mrs. Serpa switched to thoughts of optimism and hope:

"Think about it, Caio! ... Vera didn't merely entrust you with material resources for you to look after! You have considerable material assets with which to build a family ... Consider the blessings of the future! Listen to me! Whether or not you believe in God and the soul's survival after death, you have been burdened with a serious problem weighing on your mind: remorse for the murder you committed, and the memory of Tulio Mancini, stricken by your hands! You try to escape by indulging in pleasures that do not lessen your pain, and you try in vain to block out the bitter memories that constantly assail you ... To be a father, to raise beloved children, wouldn't that be the highest reward for you on earth? Your marriage to Vera will legally invest you with resources to be valued and increased, guaranteeing safety and comfort, happiness and education for your future children! ... A home, Caio! ... A home where you can rest, renew yourself, forget! ... Children in whom you can see yourself, and the company of Vera, whose presence will remind you of your mother's watch care."

In light of these holy summons to the peace and happiness that he had never experienced, for the first time in many years, Serpa wept.

Evelina continued:

"Yes, Caio. Wash your heart in the stream of your tears! ... Weep with hope, with joy! ... Let us trust in God and in life! ... The sun that sets today will rise again tomorrow! Look at these tombstones, at the graves in front of you! Everywhere, plants and flowers are bursting forth saying that death is an illusion, that life shall triumph, beautiful and eternal! ... In another world, those who love you will rejoice at your acts of understanding! Tulio will forgive you; Elisa will bless you! ... Have courage! Be brave!"

The lawyer, surprised and incapable of grasping this visit by the spirit of his wife of days gone by, suddenly felt comforted and euphoric, touched by a gentle renewal in the depths of his being.

Like a sick man who has found the medicine he needs and grabs at it in his eagerness to be healed, he instinctively decided not to lose this priceless moment of constructive exaltation.

"Go ahead!" Evelina insisted. "Reassure Vera right now that you will protect her with an authentic marriage!"

The unexpected happened.

Usually aggressive and rebellious, Caio Serpa humbly tore himself away from where he had been standing, and still embraced by his former wife's spirit, he walked over to the group that was consoling Vera ... There, helped by the thought of the spirit messenger, he looked at Vera in a new light. He felt that he had begun to love her in a different way. He found her more captivating in her suffering as he perceived her loneliness and yearning for true companionship. Suddenly, he realized how lonely he was too, and how much he needed her dedication and love in his life.

At that unforgettable moment, he didn't know whether he wanted her with the eagerness of a man or with the tenderness of a father.

He approached her and gently took her arm, and with the purpose of affirming his intentions in front of those present, he said to her:

"Don't cry anymore, Vera ... You're not alone! Tomorrow, we'll go get the documents we need and get married as soon as we can!"

Vera looked at him meaningfully and with profound gratitude. And while Caio and Vera headed home leaning on each other, Evelina and Ernesto, along with the other discarnates who had stayed for Fantini's widow's eulogy, began to pray, thanking the Lord for the blessing of that transformation.

Another important step had just been taken toward a better future.

Caio and Vera would build a home with Divine Support. Tulio Mancini would return to the earth as the son of the man who had taken his life, thereby satisfying the Law of Love that orders hatred and revenge to be banished forever from the Work of God! Later on, Elisa would join them as a beloved daughter! Caio would feel comforted, and would surely become a different man as he saw himself living on in happy posterity under the loving eye of Vera, who loved him ardently.

Evelina pondered all this in tears of joy. She continued to love her former spouse, but on a different level, and with all her heart she thanked the Lord for Vera Celina, whom she had come to love and respect during her work of assistance, and whose help she could never repay.

In a rapture of joy, Evelina ran towards the engaged couple, and before Serpa got in the car with Vera, she embraced him with gratitude, shouting for the first time into his mind with the celestial emotion of love purified through the fires of suffering:

"Caio, dearest Caio! Be happy, and may God bless you!"

Then, leaning towards Vera, she kissed her hand with infinite tenderness.

The car started back.

Evelina and Ernesto remained in prayer for a long time in the peaceful sanctuary of death, which, for them, had become a place of joy and understanding. High above, the first stars were beginning to twinkle in the forest of the night, like lanterns of fire and silver illuminating the pathway to God in the deep blue sky.

26
And Life Goes On ...

Caio and Vera's marriage brought Ernesto and Evelina a new incentive to work.

Tulio was somewhat better now due to the promise of future assistance from the woman he loved so much and he agreed to voluntarily enroll in the Reincarnation Service Institute[22], starting immediately in one of its miniaturization[23] departments for the necessary preparations.

Before starting the process, Tulio was taken to Vera one night when Serpa wasn't home so that he could get to know a bit about the woman who would receive him in her arms as a mother.

As he watched her sewing in her Vila Mariana home, Tulio immediately felt drawn to her. He noticed her gentle face, the serene eyes of someone who had suffered much, and her skillful hands at work. Enchanted, he took in the peaceful atmosphere.

---

[22] An organization on the spirit plane. – Spirit Auth.
[23] See footnote on last page of ch. 16 – Tr.

Evelina suggested that he embrace her, revering in her the caretaker who would bless him as a son in God's name ... Mancini not only embraced her lovingly, but also kissed her tenderly on the forehead.

Ernesto's daughter didn't perceive this display of love directly, but she let her mind wander in a daydream for a few moments.

"How I would love to have a son!" she thought. "How I long to be a mother!" She was awaiting this blessing from the Almighty; he surely wouldn't forget her! ... Moreover, fully aware that her husband desired an heir for the future, in her daydreams she intentionally prayed to God for a boy!

As these sweet plans for motherhood materialized in the depths of her soul, she became more intensely attuned to Tulio in the same wave of hope and jubilation; they both felt the holy prelude to unspeakable joys.

Before bidding her farewell, Tulio asked the question: Who would be his father? Who would he call dad?

Evelina hurried to explain that the head of the family was away at the moment, and that Mancini would meet him at the right time.

Based on the truth of what they had been promised, Tulio would reincarnate with Caio Serpa as his father, totally magnetized by his mother's devotion, so that he could be around his former adversary once again and transform resentment into love by means of the therapy of forgetfulness.

In light of the ongoing process, Fantini and Evelina's time was filled with pleasant and wonderful obligations: constantly supporting Mancini, Caio and Vera as they prepared for a new future, as well as providing untiring assistance to Elisa and Desiderio, who were now both suitably hospitalized.

Renewed through suffering, Ernesto seemed younger at heart, while Evelina, changed by all these new experiences, seemed to have matured; it was as if both had agreed to make adjustments in order to harmonize their ages. They shared the same ideas; they were involved in the same work.

Aware of this gradual convergence, which was the automatic result of their ever increasing and more intimate togetherness in spiritual growth, Ernesto went to see Instructor Ribas, respectfully asking if it might be possible for him to get started right away on delving into his past in order to recover the memory of other lives. His mentor, however, wisely informed him:

"No, Fantini. For now that wouldn't be advisable. You and Evelina are committed to long-time service on our plane. You will have many problems to solve and a lot of work to do ... Desiderio, Elisa, Amancio, Brigida, Caio, Vera, Tulio, Evelina and you all form a group of souls indebted to one another before the Laws of God for many centuries now ... All of you are mutually entwined in a context of expiation, much like chemical elements boiling in a crucible for the purification that is needed! Other members of the group will arrive over time for a complete victory based on the foundations of the love that is still far off! ... We are all, myself included, part of a huge family." And with a friendly smile:

"There are thousands of individuals here who are in the same situation as we are. We are all working and striving for redemption, beginning with the perfecting of ourselves in the recesses of our individual worlds."

"While on earth, we have no idea of the number of obligations waiting for us after death ..."

"No doubt. Every worthwhile undertaking must be structured. First, the planning; then, the actual execution ... In the physical realm, we idealize the continuation of life in the spirit world ... In the spirit world, we plan the correction, readjustment, improvement and betterment of this same life in the physical realm. We are travelers from cradle to grave and from grave to cradle, being reborn both on earth and in the spirit world as many times as necessary, continually learning, renewing, rectifying and progressing in conformance with the laws of the universe until we achieve perfection, our common destiny."

"This means that Evelina and I may reincarnate in the future among the very same spirits for whose improvement we are now working together."

"Who knows? It's more than possible; it's obvious ..."

The instructor had not finished his explanation when Ernesto, like a boy opening his heart to his father, stated shyly:

"Instructor Ribas, Evelina and I have been thinking ... thinking ..."

Fantini felt awkward and couldn't finish the sentence. Ribas himself completed it with good humor:

"We know that the two of you are thinking of a praiseworthy and understandable marriage, now that you are aware of the enormous task of transformation and improvement that will take place for quite some time under your guidance in the spirit group to which you are connected."

"Do you see anything keeping us from it?"

"None whatsoever, since both Elisa and Caio have already freed you from any love commitments to them."

Slightly embarrassed, Fantini was about to say something else when an assistant from the Institute summoned him to accompany Evelina to the physical world right away to assist Vera, who was now very advanced in her pregnancy.

Saying goodbye, the mentor added with a smile:

"Don't worry, Ernesto. We'll think it over."

Fantini and his companion spent their days working diligently. Little by little, they realized how many responsibilities they would have to assume in order to guarantee a relatively trouble-free rebirth for a spirit as sickly as Mancini, who required constant attention so that a miscarriage would not damage the overall plan. They realized that there were not so many concerns in thousands of other cases of reincarnation. There were spirits that adjusted to the physical world through the process of reincarnation as easily as a hand fits into a glove. In other situations, there were spirits returning to the physical sphere who were so highly evolved that their mere presence was enough to keep troublesome spirits away as well as to provide peace of mind to the mother. Tulio, however, was not among those who lightly touch the powers of the spirit in order to revel almost completely in all the pleasures and mechanisms of the physical world, nor had he reached the condition of those who simply touch dense matter only in order to seek the energy for their sustenance more than anything else in the tasks and endeavors of the spirit world. He was neither standing at the beginning of the mount of evolution nor had he reached the highest levels. He was a man of average learning and virtue, displaying acute sensibility derived from his own need of improvement in light of the debts contracted in previous lives.

Any disturbances in the maternal environment upset him, and the slightest problem led him to regrettable indispositions.

Of course, he was kept in a therapeutic sleep as part of the labor-intensive treatment for a *judiciously supervised return to the terrestrial arena,* but which, in the human realm, is simply called *pregnancy,* as if pregnancy, according to such a short and simplistic definition, were a meaningless and equal event for all *reincarnating spirits,* with analogous repercussions for the mothers who shelter them. However, it is important to recognize the fact that the spirit's therapeutic sleep, together with the fetus' development, is characterized by many degrees, and therefore is not always ruled by complete unconsciousness.

Undertakings and obligations increased on Mancini's behalf until the day when, surprised by a little boy, the ecstatic Vera and emotional Caio heard his first cries at birth.

Tulio had crossed the great divide between the two worlds, and from then on he would require a different kind of care.

Encouraged and happy with the gradual execution of the established plan, Fantini and Evelina turned their attention to the issue immediately at hand: Desiderio's return to corporeal existence.

According to the Institute's plan, it was necessary to get him set up in Amancio's house in the south of the state of Sao Paulo.

The two friends began the preparatory interviews, followed by proposals and discussions. Desiderio dos Santos begged, demanded and complained ... And the fact was that they could not immediately reveal the whole truth of what the near future held for him so that he wouldn't defy it with unjustifiable doubts or premature refusals. It was enough for him to know that he had to return to the earthly vessel and be assured that Elisa would follow him soon thereafter so that they could meet again in the material world. However, in the Institute's plan he was not allowed any information beforehand regarding the domestic dwelling in which he would start his new beginning. He had merited the blessing of reincarnation; however, it wasn't permissible for him to complicate or distort the conditions in which the ever-wise and generous authorities of the Higher Planes would assure this concession. His challenge was to live with Amancio and Brigida, just as much as the two of them, already matured by the human struggle, would have to shelter him in their home. Together, the three of them would acquire the light of mutual love in a regime of total forgetfulness so as to solidify the merit they already possessed before the Law.

Desiderio, however, was not easy to please. Questioning everything, he alleged rights in related matters of little importance, which, with Ernesto's help, his daughter tried to approve as best as possible, thereby winning his respect, acceptance, and love.

Time passed, and exactly one year after Fantini's widow had discarnated, and when Tulio Mancini was approximately two months old, Desiderio finished all his requirements for a peaceable return to the physical world except for one: he wanted to see Elisa again and talk to her by himself so that they could discuss their plans for the future.

The request was sent to Ribas and received his approval. Desiderio was then taken to the hospital where Elisa, now lucid, was convalescing and serene. The couple talked confidentially and completely alone for ten hours straight.

Nothing came to light of what they discussed in that first and last meeting in the spirit world before their reincarnation; nonetheless, something remarkable had taken place. Desiderio returned to his quarters with a new gleam in his eye. His resentment and complaints had disappeared. He was patient and respectful from then on.

Concomitantly, the former Mrs. Fantini asked for Evelina's help to enroll in a school in order to study the problems of the soul and to re-educate herself as much as possible before her return to the earthly envelope. Informed that she would be leaving for her future existence with Desiderio in three years' time under the watch care of benefactors who were sustaining them in this sphere, Elisa was anxious to learn, to prepare and to grow. She was aware that all the qualities acquired in the spirit world would transform into broader resources of support and collaboration for those who live by them, wherever they may be.

Evelina happily agreed.

During the three years that preceded the return to her own home on earth as the daughter of the Serpa couple, Elisa would be enrolled in a school suitable for her needs, under the custody and responsibility of Desiderio's daughter, whose merits and credits continued to increase at the Institute to which she had learned to serve and dedicate herself.

Who could measure the power that God had placed in the wonders of love?

Desiderio was interned in one of the miniaturization departments in preparation for his reincarnation. The authorities thought it not advisable for him to know in advance the home into which he was going to be reborn, since his condition as a surrendered child would compel him to delve deeper into examining other past lives that had justified the upcoming trial. For now, it wouldn't be useful to involve him in advanced processes of memory recall.

Fortunately, after his conversation with Elisa, Desiderio looked obviously calm and trustful, accepting all the promises he had received.

On the other hand, Ribas and his coworkers had regarded Desiderio's return to live with Amancio and Brigida as a valuable timesaver, since with the support of Divine Providence, the old acquaintances in struggle would not have to wait for him in yet another reincarnation.

Thus were the plans of rebirth on the physical plane, when Instructor Ribas invited Fantini and Evelina to meet the humble woman who would be Desiderio's mother. It would be their task to assist her as much as possible during her upcoming pregnancy, and to steer their reborn friend to the Terra household, since among the Institute collaborators and workers living near Brigida, she had accepted the responsibility of receiving him in her maternal arms, despite the extreme poverty that marked her life.

Evelina and Fantini quickly gathered information about the woman to whom they would owe so much.

She was a young woman, the wife of a farmer consumed by tuberculosis, and the mother of four children living in dire need. She herself – Dona Mariana, as she was known – was also in bad health, condemned to catching the same disease, although tuberculosis did not pose the same danger that it had in the past. It just so happened, however, that both Mariana and her husband were ending an invaluable cycle of regenerative trials on the earth and would not be able to sustain themselves for much longer in their fragile armor of flesh. Desiderio would be their last child before their discarnation, and then it would be the two spirit friends' responsibility to be his guardians, with the holy duty of creating the circumstances in which the newborn would enter the home of the old Terra couple as their adopted son.

It was late at night in the physical realm...

Mariana, her spirit freed during normal sleep[24], entered the room where Ribas and his friends were waiting.

Escorted caringly by a messenger, the newcomer could not have presented herself more humbly.

Upon finding herself with her benefactors, she came before Ribas with all the lucidity she could muster at the moment, and perhaps magnetized by his benevolent and wise look, she knelt down and asked for his blessing.

Controlling his emotions, the mentor stroked her brow, prayed to Jesus to watch over her, and said:

"Get up, Mariana, there's something we need to talk about."

---

[24] "... During sleep, the bonds that join [the spirit] to the body are loosened, and since the body does not need it while sleeping, the spirit travels through space and enters into a more direct relationship with other spirits." Allan Kardec, *The Spirits Book*, question 401. – Tr.

When she was comfortably seated, the instructor introduced her to Evelina and Ernesto, giving more emphasis to Evelina so that Mariana could keep her image imprinted on the screen of her memory upon returning to her material body.

"This is the sister who will be looking after you during your upcoming pregnancy. Please, try hard to keep her in your memory!"

The woman looked at Evelina in appreciation and pleaded:

"Angel of God, have mercy on me!"

Obviously moved, Brigida's daughter corrected her with tears in her eyes:

"I'm no angel, Mariana; just your sister!"

The young mother, whose body was resting in the world of dense matter, found herself in spirit far from the surroundings of home and gladly focused on the joy of being useful. Filled with filial affection, she turned to Ribas, with whom she had a previous understanding, and said:

"Dear father, I shall fulfill God's will by accepting one more child; I shall anticipate your watch care. My husband Joaquim is getting weaker and more sickly ... I wash and iron; I work as much as I can, but I earn very little ... Four little children! ... I don't know if you're aware of it, but rain gets into our shack ... When the wind blows through the holes in the walls, Joaquim gets worse and has coughing fits! ... I'm not complaining, my father, but I am asking for your help!"

"Oh, Mariana!" replied the instructor, touched. "Don't be afraid! God never forsakes us! Your children will be looked after, and very soon Joaquim and you will be living in a huge house."

"I trust God and I trust you!"

The selfless woman didn't realize that Ribas was referring to the couple's upcoming discarnation, when, due to genuine merit, they would live together in a new home in the Greater Life.

Mariana, now also in the care of Fantini and Evelina, went back to the wind-struck hovel. Upon reentering her body, her heart was pounding with joy. She awakened her husband:

"Joaquim! ... Joaquim!"

And with him half asleep, she told him:

"I just had a dream where I met the old man I've seen before ... He said we're going to have one more son!"

"Anything else?"

"He said we are going to have a huge house."

Unaware of the fact that she was describing something real, he laughed and added:

"Ah! Mariana! ... A huge house? Only in *another world!*

The discarnate visitors smiled ...

Evelina, moved, saw that Joaquim would not be around much longer. She prayed to the Lord for renewed strength and promised herself that she wouldn't rest until she brought Mariana and Brigida together so that Mariana's final days in that place of suffering would be mitigated by the warmth of beneficence.

Two days after the remarkable spirit meeting, Amancio's stepdaughter, supported by Fantini and with permission from higher authorities, moved into her stepfather's mansion and began to influence Brigida's maternal soul in order to achieve the anticipated objective. Evelina provided her with dreams of the little one who would come into her arms, filled her thoughts with ideals of charity and hope, suggested edifying reading materials, and inspired her to have conversations with her husband regarding the future that God would bless with the arrival of an adopted child. For the first time in the house, prayer became a regular habit. Brigida responded to her daughter's gentle influence and succeeded in getting her husband to join her in prayer every night before going to bed. Amancio consented with kindness and surprise. He was amazed at his wife's new fervor, stirred with love toward her neighbor, and because he himself practiced human solidarity, he encouraged her displays of altruism.

They planned and planned...

If God did send them an adopted son, they would treat him with all the love that filled their hearts. They would try to analyze his tendencies to steer him toward a respectable profession, and once he grew up, they would fulfill their own dream: to move to Sao Paulo[25], where he would have the best education. With that in mind, they would ask for help from Caio, their former son-in-law, who had remarried. They mostly saw each other on special occasions, but had remained friends. ... If they had a little boy ... Ever more enthusiastic and beautiful plans unfolded in those two hearts that had matured with experience.

Four months passed. Then, on a sunny morning, after the aging couple had discussed the need to assist impoverished mothers, Mariana, who lived a couple miles away, was guided by Evelina to knock on their door.

Alerted by one of her domestic workers, Brigida came to the door.

She was immediately embraced by Evelina and listened sympathetically to Mariana.

Mariana begged for a job. In a sad voice she told Brigida a bit of her story. She was pregnant again in spite of already having four children ... She had no money and her husband was very sick.

Unaware of the motive for her sudden and intense pity, Mrs. Terra gave her some money and promised to visit her later that same day as soon as her husband returned from work.

Evelina was elated with joy and confidence.

Amancio had no problem with his wife's request, and at sunset they were inside the shack. Commiserating with the poverty-

---

[25] Capital of the state of Sao Paulo. – Tr.

stricken family's situation, they saw to it that they were moved to a small but comfortable house on a plot of land they farmed.

As if he had finally found the help he had hoped for so much, Joaquim blessed his benefactors and left for the spirit world before the birth of his fifth child.

Mariana had been weakening for some time now and became gravely ill. Now a widow, she appealed to her humble relatives for help and bequeathed them four orphans in anticipation of her upcoming death.

Aghast at the worsening situation, Brigida felt increasingly more connected to her destitute sister and brought her into her own house. There, Desiderio reincarnated, at last opening his eyes to a new earthly existence.

Certain she had completed her final, sacred task, Mariana placed in the arms of her benefactors the baby they were so anxiously awaiting. She discarnated five days later!

Discarnate benefactors received the devoted mother while kissing the little one ... In the flower-surrounded house there was a mixture of farewell and arrival, sadness because of death and joy because of life! ... Brigida wept and smiled; Amancio reflected, touched by emotions and thoughts of renewal ... Ernesto and Evelina, in prayers of joyful gratitude for the mercy of Providence, noticed with wonder that to both Mariana in the coffin and Desiderio in the cradle, God had sent the blessing of a new day!

That evening a small, flying carriage in the shape of an iridescent star dropped Fantini and his companion off in their spirit colony.

They both headed for the Institute of Spiritual Watch Care, where caring and friendly souls showered them with flowers. Lampposts lit with polychromic light circled all the buildings, highlighting their architectural lines in splashes of beauty.

The place was celebrating the two workers, who, with devotion and humility, had managed to overcome all the initial difficulties in the construction of a blessed future!

Surrounded by advisors, Ribas greeted them at the door, and embracing them like beloved children, he lifted up his eyes On High and prayed:

"Lord Jesus, bless your servants, who consecrate themselves to each other today in sublime union! ... Illumine evermore their yearnings for your kingdom through the selflessness that has helped them forget difficulties and offenses, focusing only on assisting their companions of the journey, even when such companions struck them in the heart! ... O Master, teach them that happiness is an ongoing endeavor, that a marriage must be renewed every day in the domestic intimacy of a home, where our faults are extinguished through mutual tolerance so that our souls may find perfect unity before you in the light of love eternal!"

The Instructor finished, while Ernesto contemplated Evelinas's tear-drenched face.

Small garlands of blue flowers rained down from above like etherealized, radiant sapphires, providing the happy couple the certainty that the Higher Realms were endorsing their vows. From hidden corners of the surroundings came soft melodies, framed with words of trust, in which the Wisdom of the Universe confirmed the eternity of God's mercy on life as it goes on everywhere, beautiful, full of greatness, sanctified by labor, and flooded with light.

Made in the USA
Lexington, KY
06 March 2014